THE GRAND CANYON TRAIL OF TIME COMPANION

Geology Essentials for your Canyon Adventure

By the co-creators of the Trail of Time Exhibition and Grand Canyon geology researchers
Dr. Karl Karlstrom and Dr. Laura Crossey, University of New Mexico

Discover the geology behind the beauty of Grand Canyon

with
Stories from Grand Canyon's rocks (told by the rocks themselves)
and
The Making of the Trail of Time Geoscience Exhibit (1995-2010)
and
Paleogeographic Maps by Ron Blakey
and
Photographs by Michael Quinn and Laura Crossey

Table of Contents

The Trail of Time icon reflects a cyclic view of interactions between time, rocks, and erosion.

Karl Karlstrom drilling one of the 2,500 trail markers.

A timeline is a linear representation of time. What cycles can you think of that mark the passage of time?

Bronze markings define the timeline trail. Circular markers reflect a cyclic view of time.

Preface to The Grand Canyon Trail of Time Companion.

We wrote the *Companion* for all audiences, no matter your age. It is designed to enhance your visit to the Trail of Time Exhibition at Grand Canyon National Park. The content is authoritative and up-to-date, generated by active Grand Canyon researchers. It provides Grand Canyon's geology essentials for all. As one visitor said during our prototyping of the exhibition: *"You can read it in a book, but your eyes glaze over. It's better in little bits along the Trail."*

The experience of viewing Grand Canyon is inexplicably transformative for the artist, photographer, poet, and scientist in you. The Trail of Time may help you appreciate the geology behind its beauty. Geology forms the backdrop for ecosystems, the water we drink, and all Park resources. Grand Canyon experiences seem to be a merging of the beauty, the grand spatial dimension, and the deep time dimension. We are taken out of the present, out of ourselves, to encounter new possibilities. The Trail of Time enhances these adventures.

The goals of this Grand Canyon Trail of Time Companion are as varied as you are. The walk itself is a memorable hike. It is paved, fairly flat, and most of it is fully accessible. It offers unparalleled and changing views, time and space for contemplation, with outdoor elements of sun, wind, weather. You may want to walk just few hundred meters from one of the entry portals to get great views. But beware, the bronze markers are "bread crumbs" that will lure you on through time. Design your hike to match your schedule. If you walk the entire 2 km (1.24 miles) between Yavapai Geology Museum and Grand Canyon Village, the timeline takes you through all of Grand Canyon's rocks, and half of our planet's history. A common reaction is: *"That was a lot of steps, the Earth must be really old."*

Families, groups, and individuals will find activities in this guide that combine sightseeing, learning, challenges, and adventure. Kids love to hop on and count the markers and touch the rocks. Wayside signs are conversational such that you get the main points even on a jog such as: *"People have lived here for over 10,000 years."* The real rocks were brought out of the canyon for you to see and touch and each placed at its age ("birthday") on the timeline. Their fascinating stories are told here as if by the rocks themselves "in the first person" with kids in mind.

The nuts and bolts of using this guide are similar to those used by river runners on the Colorado River — follow along as you go, drink in the views and the experience. The *Companion* enriches your journey. Pages are color-coded for the segment(s) of the Trail you choose to walk. The entry portals visually portray a main geologic concept: *"Grand Canyon is a young canyon carved into very old rocks."* PLEASE TOUCH THEM; they are getting more polished each year from your attention.

Overview: What is the Trail of Time? *It's A Geology Timeline.*

The Trail of Time is the world's largest geoscience exhibition at the world's grandest geologic landscape, Grand Canyon National Park. The Trail of Time helps you utilize the unique vistas and rocks of Grand Canyon to *ponder, explore, and understand* the magnitude of geologic time and the stories encoded by Grand Canyon rocks and landscapes. Earth is REALLY old, so geologic time is immensely long. The trail is marked every meter. At 1 meter = 1 million years it takes 4,560 long steps to walk through the 4.56 billion years of Earth's history.

The Trail of Time is on the South Rim of Grand Canyon National Park. It extends 4.6 km (about 3 mile) along the paved Rim Trail between the Yavapai Geology Museum on the east and Maricopa Point on the west. Most of the Trail of Time is accessible to wheelchairs and baby strollers, and convenient to shuttle bus stops and parking areas. You can park at Grand Canyon Village, Park Headquarters, Yavapai Geology Museum, or the Visitors Center, walk any segment of the Trail of Time forward or backward through time, and catch a shuttle bus back. It makes a great hike.

Bronze markers tell where you are in time, and divide time into million-year steps.

Start at any of the 4 entry/exit portals. These were made from the real Grand Canyon rocks.

17 wayside panels tell about Grand Canyon's history and geologic processes.

Folded Vishnu basement rock

46 rock samples were collected along the river and placed at their age along the timeline.

Viewing tubes show you how to connect the rocks in the Canyon walls to their place along the timeline.

How to walk the Trail of Time? It has 3 segments.

③ The Early Earth Trail picks up west of Grand Canyon Village near the Hermits Rest shuttle stop. Look for the 2,930-million-year marker and the steps to the west Rim Trail. This trail is marked every 10 meters to the 4,560-million-year age of the Earth. The Early Earth Trail is a more challenging hike with spectacular views, but it is not fully accessible. You can walk just past Maricopa Point to Powell Point to catch the shuttle bus back to the Village.

② The Main Trail of Time. On this trail, each meter (each long step) represents one million years. Your progress is shown by small bronze markers every meter and a numbered marker every 10 million years. This 2-km-long (1.24 mile) segment takes you from the carving of Grand Canyon in the past 6 million years (six steps) to the oldest rock unit in Grand Canyon, the 1,840-million-year-old Elves Chasm gneiss. If you want to walk from oldest to youngest, walk from Verkamps Visitor Center two thousand steps (2 billion years) to Yavapai Geology Museum. You can catch the shuttle bus at either end and also near the middle (with a 0.6 km (0.4 mi) walk to Park Headquarters).

① The Million Year Trail is also called the "Time Accelerator," or the "ON RAMP." From Yavapai Geology Museum, tour the museum then walk to the portal about 200 meters west of Yavapai Museum. It starts with HUMAN TIME (one step = one year), then accelerates to 1 step = 10, 100, 1,000, 10,000, and 100,000 years into deep time. On this trail, each meter is marked with a numbered disk. When you have walked a million years on this trail, you can think about how human time scales relate to geologic time.

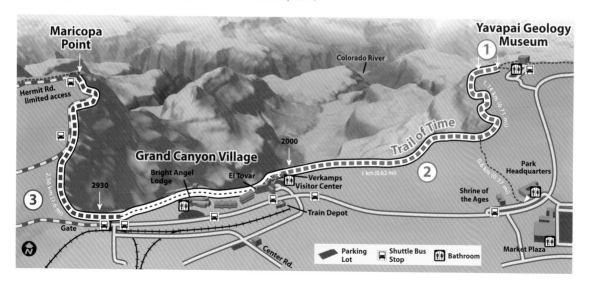

How long does it take, what will I see, what should I bring?

Time spent on the rim of Grand Canyon may be one of the best ways to spend your next hour(s). You can start at Yavapai Geology Museum (recommended) or Verkamps Visitor Center in Grand Canyon Village. After viewing the museum, head out the west door, walk 200 m (650 feet) to the first portal, then another 170 m (560 ft) to complete the Million Year Trail. It takes about an hour. This gets you thinking about geologic time and how humans fit it. The Main Trail of Time proceeds another 2 km (1.24 miles) west on the rim trail and is marked at 1 meter = 1 million years. You can exit after a billion years (1.4 km from Yavapai) at the Headquarters Trail junction OR, walk the second billion years (another 1 km or 0.6 mile) to historic Grand Canyon Village. It is another 2.5 km (1.5 miles) to the age of the Earth at Maricopa Point, but that might be another trip. If you do the Main Trail of Time (from Yavapai to the Village or vice versa) it is 2.14 km (1.3 mile) and will take 2-3 hours, you'll see all of the rock exhibits and most wayside signs, and you can catch a shuttle bus to your next destination. It is recommended to take water, a hat, proper shoes and clothes for weather changes, and a snack for along the Trail.

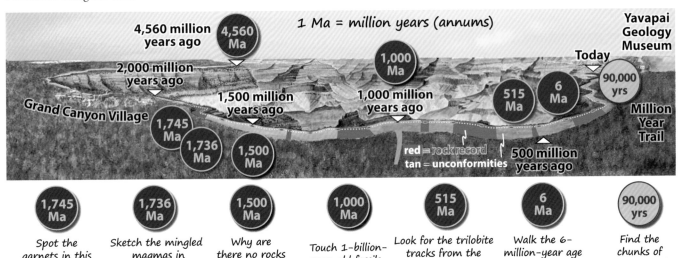

4,560 million years ago — 4,560 Ma

1 Ma = million years (annums)

Yavapai Geology Museum

2,000 million years ago

1,000 Ma

Today

90,000 yrs

Grand Canyon Village

1,500 million years ago

1,000 million years ago

515 Ma

6 Ma

Million Year Trail

1,745 Ma

1,736 Ma

1,500 Ma

red = rock record
tan = unconformities

500 million years ago

1,745 Ma	1,736 Ma	1,500 Ma	1,000 Ma	515 Ma	6 Ma	90,000 yrs
Spot the garnets in this metamorphic rock.	Sketch the mingled magmas in this igneous rock.	Why are there no rocks near this marker?	Touch 1-billion-year-old fossils.	Look for the trilobite tracks from the Cambrian explosion.	Walk the 6-million-year age of Grand Canyon.	Find the chunks of Earth's mantle.

Basics for your journey.

The flat-lying strata are the Paleozoic rocks. They range from 510 to 270 million years old.

150 million years are missing here within the flat-lying strata (a disconformity).

Up to 600 million years are missing here; layers below were tilted before upper layers were deposited (an angular unconformity).

The tilted strata are the Grand Canyon Supergroup. They range from 1,250 to 729 million years old.

About 500 million years are missing here; erosion exhumed igneous and metamorphic basement rocks from great depth to the surface (a nonconformity).

The Vishnu basement rocks are metamorphic rocks and granite intrusions. They range from 1.84 to 1.66 billion years old.

Touch the rocks and use the magnifier on your cell phone to zoom in and see their beauty!

How to Use This Companion.

Watch for italicized letters like this that mark activities, quotes, and questions to ponder.

Where we abbreviate "million years" and "billion years", we use "metric" time:
a= annum (a year)
ka= kilo annum (a thousand years)
Ma= mega annum (a million years)
Ga= giga annum (a billion years)

Rocks are dated mainly using the mineral zircon that occurs both in volcanic layers and as sand-sized grains in the sediments (see p. 120). These ages continue to get refined by new research.

Geologists are the detectives that unravel rock stories (what happened when, and how). Rocks are named for places near them. The layers are called formations (and members). Related formations are lumped into groups and supergroups (see p. 57).

Medallions in the outside corners help you relate things you see along the Trail of Time to information and stories in the *Companion*.

THE MILLION YEAR TRAIL

From the main Grand Canyon Visitors Center and Mather Point, walk west to find the Yavapai Geology Museum. From Yavapai Geology Museum, walk west about 200 meters to find the Million Year Portal and the Time Zero (Today) bronze marker that starts the Million Year Trail at its young end.

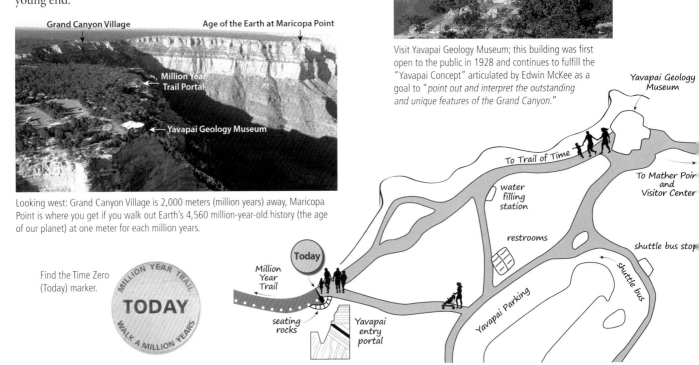

Grand Canyon Village

Age of the Earth at Maricopa Point

Million Year Trail Portal

Yavapai Geology Museum

Looking west: Grand Canyon Village is 2,000 meters (million years) away, Maricopa Point is where you get if you walk out Earth's 4,560 million-year-old history (the age of our planet) at one meter for each million years.

Visit Yavapai Geology Museum; this building was first open to the public in 1928 and continues to fulfill the "Yavapai Concept" articulated by Edwin McKee as a goal to "*point out and interpret the outstanding and unique features of the Grand Canyon.*"

Find the Time Zero (Today) marker.

MILLION YEAR TRAIL
TODAY
WALK A MILLION YEARS

Million Year Trail

Today

seating rocks

Yavapai entry portal

To Trail of Time

water filling station

restrooms

Yavapai Parking

Yavapai Geology Museum

To Mather Point and Visitor Center

shuttle bus stop

shuttle bus

Secrets of the Million Year Trail portal.

Around the Million Year Trail portal are examples of the youngest rocks of the Grand Canyon region– about 500,000 years old to present. The pavers are travertine, formed as spring-deposited limestones. These are "imports" from New Mexico, but they are similar to the youngest rocks in Grand Canyon that are forming today from bubbling blue spring water in Havasu Creek and the Little Colorado River.

The smaller basalt column is from western Grand Canyon; it is 550,000 years old. The larger column next to it is "an import" from the Columbia River basalts in Oregon. The hexagonal shape forms during cooling of basalt and is called columnar jointing.

Looking up at columnar joints in basalt of western Grand Canyon.

Today

Walk a million years on this timeline trail.

To humans a million years seems unimaginably long, more than 10,000 lifetimes. This trail helps you shift from human time to geologic time.

Talk about time as you walk the trail.

TIME
- **Years** — your birthday
- **Decades** — your generation
- **Centuries** — U.S. history
- **Millennia** — ancient peoples
- **10,000s** — changing climate
- **100,000s** — earthquakes and volcanoes
- **Millions** — a six million year old Grand Canyon
- **Billions** — oldest rocks in Grand Canyon

Imagine
one million.

That's how many steps it is from here to the California coast.

Find your birthday.

As you walk the trail, think of all that happened before your time.

To Park Headquarters

Grand Canyon Village

We SQUEEZE time along this trail so you don't have to walk a million steps!

YOU ARE HERE

1 million

20 YEARS AGO

Parking

40   50   60   100   1,000   10,000   100,000

30

Today   10

0.2 km (0.1 mi) to Yavapai Geology Museum   2.1 km (1.3 mi) to Grand Canyon Village

Yavapai Geology Museum

20 yrs

The Million Year trail is an on-ramp to the Trail of Time, a time accelerator.

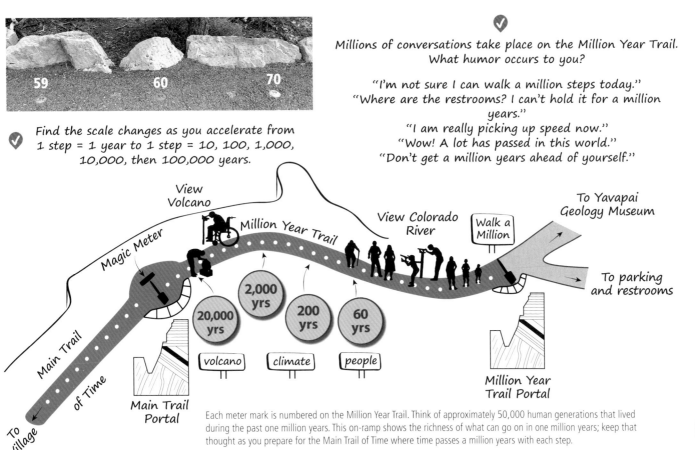

59   60   70

Find the scale changes as you accelerate from 1 step = 1 year to 1 step = 10, 100, 1,000, 10,000, then 100,000 years.

Millions of conversations take place on the Million Year Trail. What humor occurs to you?

"I'm not sure I can walk a million steps today."
"Where are the restrooms? I can't hold it for a million years."
"I am really picking up speed now."
"Wow! A lot has passed in this world."
"Don't get a million years ahead of yourself."

View Volcano

Magic Meter

Million Year Trail

View Colorado River

Walk a Million

To Yavapai Geology Museum

To parking and restrooms

Main Trail

of Time

To Village

Main Trail Portal

20,000 yrs

2,000 yrs

200 yrs

60 yrs

volcano   climate   people

Million Year Trail Portal

Each meter mark is numbered on the Million Year Trail. Think of approximately 50,000 human generations that lived during the past one million years. This on-ramp shows the richness of what can go on in one million years; keep that thought as you prepare for the Main Trail of Time where time passes a million years with each step.

20 yrs

The Colorado River carries water for the Southwest.

The Colorado River gets its water from the Rockies and carries it across the arid Colorado Plateau and deserts of the Basin and Range. Major tributaries

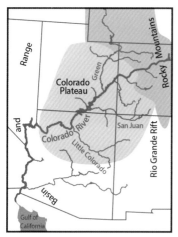

include the Green River, Gunnison, San Juan, and Little Colorado. The river continues to carve Grand Canyon and other deep canyons along its path. Today, it supplies water for the Southwest but its flow is unable to meet growing demands.

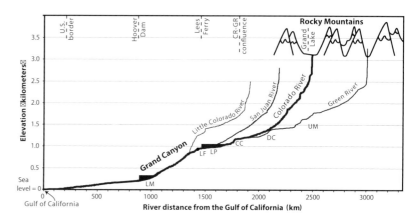

In profile view, the Colorado River and its tributaries have steep gradients in the Rocky Mountains and are flat near the sea.[2] The steepness through Grand Canyon produces major rapids.

Colorado River

The first viewing tube gives a small glimpse of the mighty Colorado River visible from this marker. It looks small but the river has powerful current, huge rapids, and great stream power — enough to carve through solid rock.

Grand Canyon's springs and groundwater.

Springs emerge from water-bearing rock layers called aquifers that have been incised by canyon cutting. South Rim springs are recharged by snowmelt from the San Francisco Peaks, near Flagstaff. North Rim springs are recharged from snowmelt on the Kaibab uplift. The main water-bearing (aquifer) units are the Redwall-Muav aquifer and the Kaibab-Coconino aquifer. Water types and quality differ depending on mixtures of "upper world" recharge and "lower world" naturally-carbonated, magmatically sourced waters. The flow paths and chemistry of groundwaters are affected by both faults and aquifer pathways. South Rim Village and the Park are supplied by groundwaters from Roaring Springs on North Rim that are cold and fresh (and low in lower world components); this water is piped across the canyon to the South Rim (see page 126). What an engineering feat and continued challenge.

Blue waters of the spring-fed Little Colorado River merge with green waters of the Colorado River; imagine such mixing taking place in subsurface groundwaters too.

Blue Springs is the source of the Little Colorado River. It emerges from near the top of the Redwall Limestone. Its baseflow is about 100,000 gallons per minute but that gets over-run by ten times that much red muddy water during springtime and summer monsoon floods.

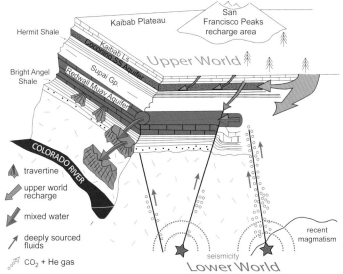

Hermit Shale

Bright Angel Shale

Kaibab Plateau

San Francisco Peaks recharge area

Kaibab Ls.

Coconino SS Aquifer

Supai Gp.

Redwall Muav Aquifer

Upper World

COLORADO RIVER

travertine

upper world recharge

mixed water

deeply sourced fluids

CO_2 + He gas

seismicity

recent magmatism

Lower World

'Upper World' versus 'Lower World' waters; they mix in the aquifer to produce diverse water types and water quality in Grand Canyon.[3,4]

48 yrs

MORE ON THIS TOPIC

People have lived here for over 10,000 years.

Today, at least 12 Native American tribes think of Grand Canyon as part of their homeland. The canyon's grandeur attracts millions of visitors each year from all over the world.

Find — MILLION YEAR TRAIL — **150 YEARS AGO** — WALK A MILLION YEARS

John Wesley Powell
led the first geologic exploration through Grand Canyon in 1869.

Find — MILLION YEAR TRAIL — **1,000 YEARS AGO** — WALK A MILLION YEARS

Ancestral Puebloans farmed the canyon bottom.
These rooms were used to store their crops.

Find — MILLION YEAR TRAIL — **4,000 YEARS AGO** — WALK A MILLION YEARS

Paleo-Indians made split-twig figures.
These 4,000-year-old figurines have been found in caves. They are some of the oldest human-made artifacts in Grand Canyon.

Find — MILLION YEAR TRAIL — **10,000 YEARS AGO** — WALK A MILLION YEARS

Nomadic hunters lived here 10,000 years ago.
They may have influenced the extinction of large mammals like the Shasta Sloth.

To Park Headquarters

Grand Canyon Village

YOU ARE HERE

1,000 YEARS AGO

We SQUEEZE time along this trail so you don't have to walk a million steps!

Parking

Today

10   20   30   40   50   60   100   10,000   100,000   1 million

0.3 km (0.2 mi) to Yavapai Geology Museum

2.1 km (1.3 mi) to Grand Canyon Village

Yavapai Geology Museum

✓ Ask your group to imagine living in Grand Canyon at different times in the past 10,000 years. What a place to explore; what a place to raise a family!

John Wesley Powell in 1869 at age 35 led the first scientific exploration of the Colorado River system. He also explored the rim regions and learned the languages and customs of Native Americans.[5,6]

Tusayan Ruin on the East Rim Drive was a small village of about 30 people who lived near the rim of Grand Canyon. It looked something like this in the late 1100s.[7] The San Francisco Peaks are in the background. Illustration by Roy Anderson.

Do you think of human lifetimes as insignificant compared to geologic time? In what ways do we embody the culmination of a long human history? What are our responsibilities for those who will come after us?

The oldest known people of the region lived here between 11,500 and 8,000 years ago. They lived during the last ice age and hunted mountain goats, ground sloth, and bison with spear points like this Folsom point from Grand Canyon National Park's collections.

1,000 yrs

MORE ON THIS TOPIC

Climate changes affect ecology, geology, and you.

20,000 years ago, Grand Canyon was in a much cooler and wetter climate cycle.

Imagine how past global climate cycles affected Grand Canyon.

Future?

Warmer and dryer times were similar to today's climate and vegetation.

Today

100,000 years ago

200,000 years ago

20,000 years ago

Cooler and wetter times had heavily forested canyon walls.

Warmer, Dryer

Cooler, Wetter

Find the bands in trees and rocks.
Nature records climate change in these bands.

10 years old   50 years old

Tree rings record 10s to 1000s of years.

354,000 years old

Cave deposits and spring deposits record 1,000s to 100,000s of years.

To Park Headquarters

Grand Canyon Village

YOU ARE HERE

20,000 YEARS AGO

million

We SQUEEZE time along this trail so you don't have to walk a million steps!

40   50   60   100   1,000   10,000   100,000

30

Parking

20

Today   10

0.28 km (0.17 mi) to Yavapai Geology Museum

2.05 km (1.27 mi) to Grand Canyon Village

Yavapai Geology Museum

20,000 yrs

Climate change takes place at many timescales.

Climate changes get recorded in different ways: by historical records, the rings of trees, by ice cores on polar icecaps, and by some rocks such as speleothems in caves and travertines. Higher carbon dioxide (CO_2) in the atmosphere leads to greenhouse conditions and global warming; warming causes ice on the polar icecaps to melt and sea level to rise. Glaciers have not covered the Grand Canyon region, but it was cooler and wetter here during global glacial times than during the present interglacial period. At the 100-year timescale, global CO_2 and temperature measurements suggest an alarming rate of warming.

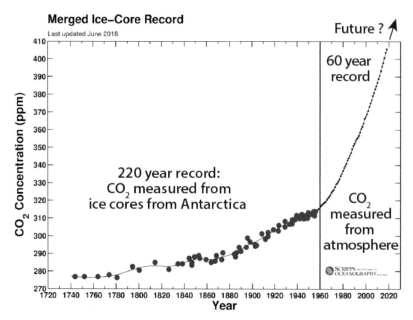

Merged Ice–Core Record
Last updated June 2018

220 year record:
CO_2 measured from
ice cores from Antarctica

60 year record

CO_2 measured from atmosphere

Future ?

SCRIPPS INSTITUTION OF OCEANOGRAPHY

Travertines are the youngest rocks in Grand Canyon.[3] This sample was collected at Elves Chasm where spring water has been depositing travertine over much of the past million years. Its bands record cyclic changes in wet versus dry intervals.

The global carbon dioxide record over the past 300 years[8] comes from combining continuous direct atmospheric CO_2 measurements (black dots) back to 1958 from South Pole and Mauna Loa Observatory in Hawaii with measurements of gases in ice-cores of Antarctica (blue dots, before 1960). These data show clearly that global atmospheric CO_2 concentration is increasing at faster and faster rates; what will it do in the future?

"Looking back across the long cycles of change through which the land has been shaped into its present form, let us realize that these geographical revolutions are not events wholly of the dim past, but that they are still in progress."
Sir Archibald Geikie (1905)[9]

20,000 yrs

The Million Year Trail

Eruptions and earthquakes may happen here again.

100,000 years ago volcanoes erupted west of here. Even today, volcanoes, earthquakes and erosion work together to shape this spectacular landscape.

Lava flows dammed the Colorado River.

Volcanoes, like this one, sent lava flows cascading into Grand Canyon.

A timeline of volcanism in the western Grand Canyon

today
1,000 to 100,000 years ago
200,000 to 350,000 years ago
500,000 to 650,000 years ago

Vulcan's Throne volcano, 100 km (60 mi) west of here.

Imagine viewing an eruption!

Pottery fragments have been found in 1,000-year-old lava flows suggesting that people witnessed these eruptions.

pottery fragment

Find the locations of recent Grand Canyon earthquakes.

○ Earthquakes recorded in the last 20 years.

You Are Here

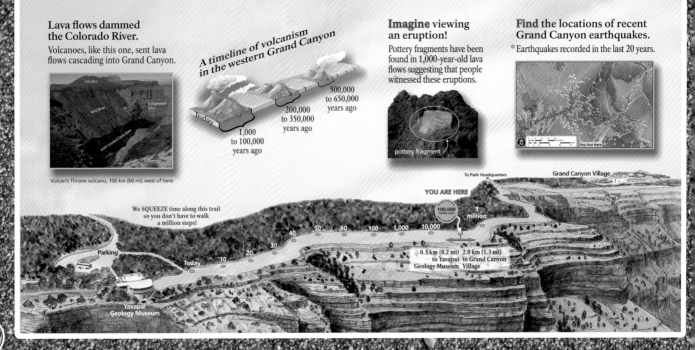

To Park Headquarters

Grand Canyon Village

YOU ARE HERE

100,000 YEARS AGO

1 million

10,000

1,000

100

60

50

40

30

20

10

We SQUEEZE time along this trail so you don't have to walk a million steps!

Today

Parking

0.3 km (0.2 mi) to Yavapai Geology Museum

2.0 km (1.3 mi) to Grand Canyon Village

Yavapai Geology Museum

100,000 yrs

Grand Canyon is part of a tectonically active landscape.

Imagine the volcanic eruptions that took place repeatedly in western Grand Canyon in the past 600,000 years. Lavas flowed into Grand Canyon and dammed the Colorado River more than 17 times.[10,11,12] San Francisco Volcano near Flagstaff built into a major stratovolcano over the past several million years. Native people witnessed volcanic eruptions in both places, the youngest are only about 1,000 years old! Earthquakes also rattle the region — usually low magnitudes (2-4 on the Richter scale).[13] Both the volcanism and the earthquakes are signals of a tectonically active region that is likely to undergo more exciting geological events in the near future.

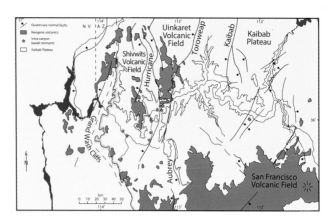

Uinkaret volcanoes

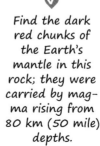

The view tube at the 190,000 year marker focuses on the distant Uinkaret volcanoes on the western horizon. The William Henry Holmes lithograph from the Dutton 1882 USGS folio[14] shows what it looks like; basalts were frozen in place as they poured down existing canyons. Imagine how the 1,000-year-old pottery fragment pictured on the sign was frozen into one of the lavas.

Find the dark red chunks of the Earth's mantle in this rock; they were carried by magma rising from 80 km (50 mile) depths.

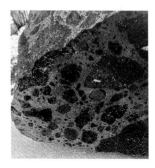

190,000 yrs

The Million Year Trail

This bronze meter represents the last million years.

← Walk this way to feel how long 2,000 million (2 billion) years is. One long step = 1 million years.

Walk this way to see what happened in the last million years. →

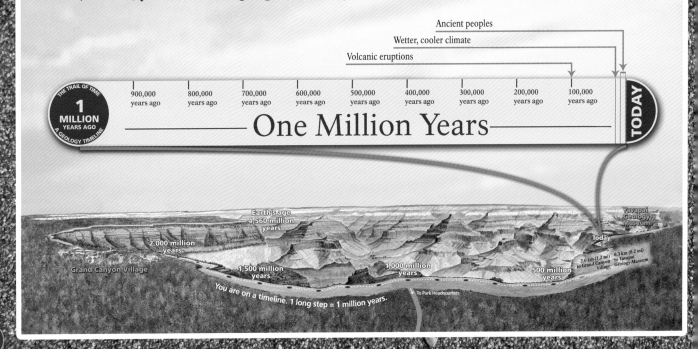

Ancient peoples

Wetter, cooler climate

Volcanic eruptions

THE TRAIL OF TIME
1 MILLION YEARS AGO
A GEOLOGY TIMELINE

900,000 years ago
800,000 years ago
700,000 years ago
600,000 years ago
500,000 years ago
400,000 years ago
300,000 years ago
200,000 years ago
100,000 years ago

One Million Years

TODAY

Earth's age 4,560 million years

2,000 million years

Grand Canyon Village

1,500 million years

You are on a timeline. 1 long step = 1 million years.

To Park Headquarters

1,000 million years

500 million years

Today

Yavapai Geology Museum

2.0 km (1.2 mi) to Grand Canyon Village
0.3 km (0.2 mi) to Yavapai Geology Museum

1 Ma

The Magic Meter encodes events of the past 1 million years.

Walking 0.3 km (0.2 mi) from here to Yavapai Geology Museum explores just the last one million years. But from here to Grand Canyon Village, a million years is compressed into a single, one meter step. The magic meter reminds us just how much happens in each of those million-year steps!

 Can you find the 3 paving slabs with fossil trackways that are shown with stars in this picture?

The paving stones and seating stones at this portal are from the Coconino Sandstone — symbolic of the flat-lying sedimentary rock layers.

Walking west- finishing the Million Year Trail and starting the Main Trail of Time.

Walking east, finishing the Main Trail of Time and starting the Million Year Trail.

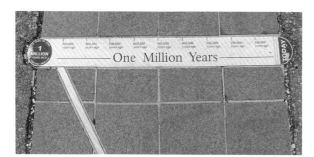

The long diagonal connects the end of the Million Year Trail with the start of the Main Trail of Time. The bronze meter shows how the entire Million Year Trail would fit into the Main Trail of Time.

THE MAIN TRAIL OF TIME

The Main Trail of Time portals reveal the 3 sets of rocks.[15]

1) **Flat-lying sedimentary layers:** The Paleozoic (ancient life) Era was from 541 to 252 million years ago and the 1-km-thickness of Grand Canyon layers record about half of this time. To remember the rock names, use this mnemonic: **K**now **T**he **C**anyon's **H**istory, **S**tudy **R**ocks **M**ade **B**y **T**ime. The first letter of each word stands for **K**aibab Limestone, **T**oroweap Formation, **C**oconino Sandstone, **H**ermit Formation, **S**upai Group, **R**edwall Limestone, **M**uav Limestone, **B**right Angel Shale, and **T**apeats Sandstone. Fossils entombed in the layers record the evolution of life such as shelled marine animals, early fish, and early land plants.

2) **Tilted sedimentary layers are the Grand Canyon Supergroup:**[16,17] Unkar Group (1255–1100 Ma) and Chuar Group (780–729 Ma) are each about 2 km thick but are shown at half scale in the portals. All are sedimentary layers except the Cardenas Basalt, the black layer. Originally flat-lying, the layers were tilted into fault blocks. These rocks contain the oldest fossils in the Grand Canyon (stromatolites) where single-celled life built algal colonies in the Bass Formation.

3) **Precambrian Vishnu Basement**[18] records the assembly of the continent — 1.84 to 1.66 billion years ago. These rocks have a profound verticality formed by vertical foliation (metamorphic layering) and vertical magma. The 1.75 billion-year-old Rama, Brahma, and Vishnu schists were deposited on an older basement of 1.84 billion-year-old Elves Chasm gneiss, then were intruded by granite intrusions like the Zoroaster granite. These rocks were deformed during mountain building (orogeny) in which crust was squeezed, folded, thickened, and metamorphosed in a plate collision zone during the assembly of this part of the North American continent. Basement rocks were metamorphosed at 20 km beneath now-eroded mountain tops. As the mountains were eroded, basement rocks were exhumed to reach the surface by the time the Bass Formation was deposited 1.25 billion years ago.

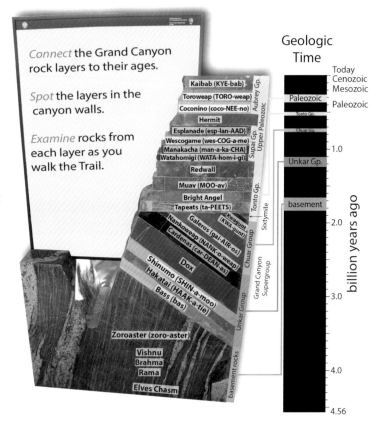

Connect the Grand Canyon rock layers to their ages.

Spot the layers in the canyon walls.

Examine rocks from each layer as you walk the Trail.

Connect, Touch, and Examine Time and Rock — the <u>rock</u> column in Grand Canyon looks amazingly complete (a vertical mile of rock), but the <u>time</u> column shows that there is more time "missing" (black) than recorded. What percentage of Earth history would you say is recorded (not black) in the Geologic Time column?

The Main Trail of Time: 1 long step = 1 million years.

It's a timeline!

The timeline at your feet always tells you were you are IN TIME. The "tens" markers tell how many millions of years ago (and how many steps you have taken).

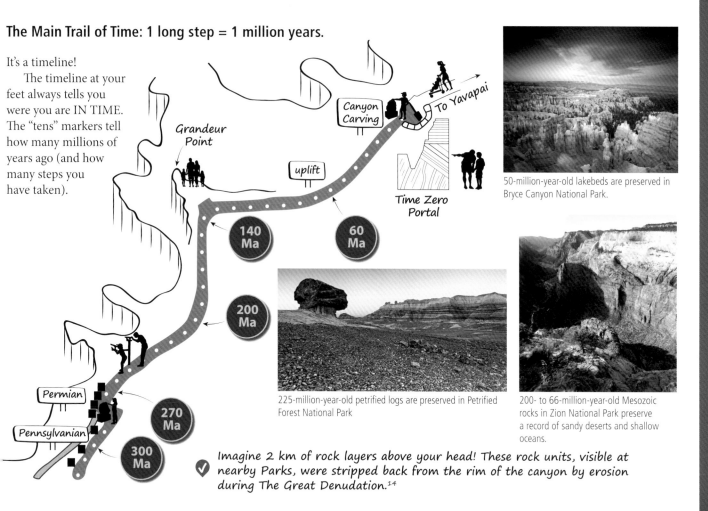

Grandeur Point

uplift

Canyon Carving

To Yavapai

Time Zero Portal

140 Ma

60 Ma

200 Ma

Permian

Pennsylvanian

270 Ma

300 Ma

50-million-year-old lakebeds are preserved in Bryce Canyon National Park.

225-million-year-old petrified logs are preserved in Petrified Forest National Park

200- to 66-million-year-old Mesozoic rocks in Zion National Park preserve a record of sandy deserts and shallow oceans.

✓ Imagine 2 km of rock layers above your head! These rock units, visible at nearby Parks, were stripped back from the rim of the canyon by erosion during The Great Denudation.[14]

MORE ON THIS TOPIC ▶

Grand Canyon is 6 million years old.

The Colorado River carved Grand Canyon in "only" the last six million years. This is a short time period compared to the age of the rocks in the canyon walls.

Touch a river polished rock.

This rock, brought from deep in the Grand Canyon, was shaped and eroded by the powerful Colorado River.

Imagine carving the canyon.

The Colorado River carves through solid rock. It carves away the thickness of a piece of paper each year. The canyon widens as cliffs fall down and side streams erode.

Walk six long steps.

These steps represent the 6 million years it has taken the Colorado River to carve Grand Canyon.

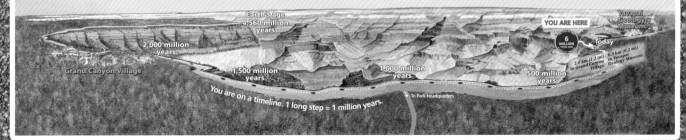

Earth's age 4,560 million years

2,000 million years

Grand Canyon Village

1,500 million years

1,000 million years

500 million years

YOU ARE HERE

6 MILLION YEARS AGO

Today

2.0 km (1.2 mi) to Grand Canyon Village

0.3 km (0.2 mi) to Yavapai Geology Museum

Yavapai Geology Museum

You are on a timeline. 1 long step = 1 million years.

To Park Headquarters

6 Ma

Canyon Carving in the First Six Steps.

Grand Canyon is a geologically "young" canyon carved in the past six million years into very old rocks.

Q. **How old:** When did snowmelt (water and sediment) from the Rocky Mountains first get transported by the Colorado River to the Gulf of California?

A. The Colorado River did not cross the western boundary of modern Grand Canyon (the Grand Wash Cliffs) before six million years ago, and its sediments (the Bouse Formation) appeared in the Gulf of California five million years ago.[19,20,21,22]

Q. How fast is the Colorado River cutting the Grand Canyon?

A. The river cuts down at about the thickness of a piece of paper (0.2 mm) every year; through time this amounts to 200 meters per million years and about 1 km of rock incision in 5 million years.[23]

Q. How did Grand Canyon get so wide?

A. The canyon widens as tributaries eat into the walls. Gravity, landslides and debris flows carry rocks to the tributaries, tributaries carve mainly during energetic flash floods, the river carries the sediment to the sea like a conveyor belt.

Q. Are there any deeper or longer or wider canyons on Earth?

A. Yes, but none as grand.

Q. How are major rivers "born?"

A. Rivers develop by uplift of headwaters, subsidence of base level, and integration of smaller river segments.[22]

River-polished rocks remind us of the power of the river (and time).

 Touch me and imagine how much time it took the Colorado River to shape this basement rock.

6 Ma

How old is Grand Canyon? Get to know the evidence from the modern landscape.

Above Lees Ferry is Canyonlands country, carved from younger rocks of the Mesozoic Era. At Lees Ferry, the Colorado first cuts into the Kaibab Limestone, the rim rock of Grand Canyon. The south-flowing Colorado River through Marble Canyon makes a right turn to the west across the Kaibab uplift. Eastern Grand Canyon, between North and South Rim, is a mile deep (1.6 km) and more than 10 miles wide (16 km). Other segments are very narrow (Marble Canyon and Muav Gorge) and some wider (Hurricane fault and Western segments). The Grand Canyon ends amazingly abruptly where the Colorado River emerges through the Grand Wash cliffs, leaves the Colorado Plateau, and enters the Basin and Range. There was no Colorado River here before six million years ago. Only after that time do Colorado River deposits appear in the Lake Mead area. Traces of earlier landscapes can be seen today. Hindu and Peach Springs paleocanyons contain 65 million year old gravels.[24] Remnants of lava flows at Red Butte (9.2 Ma) and the Shivwits Plateau (5-9 Ma) preserve pre-Grand Canyon erosion levels[25] whereas Uinkaret lava flows cascaded into Grand Canyon over the past 800 thousand years.[12]

Map labels: Grand Staircase, Lake Powell, Canyon, Kanab, Vermillion Cliffs, Lees Ferry, Hurricane Cliffs, Uinkaret Plateau, Kaibab Uplift, Marble Canyon, Echo Cliffs, Grand Wash Cliffs, Muav Gorge, North Rim, Little Colorado River, Lake Mead, Shivwits Plateau, Eastern, Pearce Ferry, Western, Hurricane, Havasu Canyon, South Rim, Sky Walk, Red Butte, Hindu paleocanyons, Peach Springs, paleocanyon, Aubrey Cliffs, San Francisco Volcanic Field

How would one date the "age" of the "negative space" of a canyon?

How old is Grand Canyon? — the paleocanyon solution.

Rivers, canyons, and landscapes are continually changing. Geologists and visitors alike seek to understand the modern landscape in order to also unravel older ones (and envision future ones). Long-known geologic constraints for the age of Grand Canyon include: 1) 65-million-year-old rivers flowed north in Hindu paleocanyon to the Hurricane segment of Grand Canyon.[24] 2) Hopi paleolake existed 15 million years ago in a Little Colorado paleovalley that had been partly carved.[25] 3) The Colorado River did not pass through Grand Wash cliffs until after 6 million years ago (Muddy Creek constraint).[20, 21] New technologies can determine when rocks become exposed due to erosion of overlying layers (thermochronology; see p. 120). These data show that the Little Colorado paleoriver carved across Kaibab uplift between 25

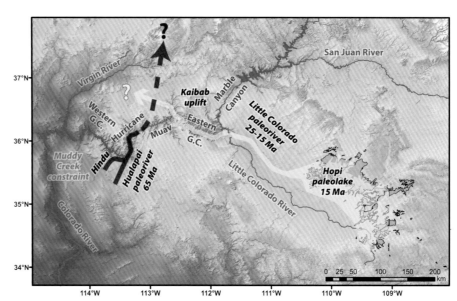

"Old" (65 Ma) and "intermediate" (25-15 Ma) paleocanyon segments existed in the pre-6 million year old landscapes and these were still low spots that got linked together by the Colorado River to carve Grand Canyon as we see it today in the past 6 million years.[27]

and 15 million years ago, but that Marble, Muav, and Western segments of Grand Canyon were not carved until after 6 million years.[26] Thus, the paleocanyon solution to the age of Grand Canyon[27] is that older paleocanyons existed that got linked together by the Colorado River about 6 million years ago as it became integrated from the Rocky Mountains to the Gulf of California. Today, the Colorado River and its side canyons have the stream power needed to carve any rock type; they are efficient "buzz saws." They use steep gradients, floods, and abrasive sediments to incise through rock. A multitude of erosional processes (including landslides and rockfalls) help the tributaries widen the canyon.

MORE ON THIS TOPIC

Main Trail of Time

Without uplift there would be no Grand Canyon.

The Colorado Plateau region was lifted high above sea level. The high elevation set the stage for the later carving of Grand Canyon.

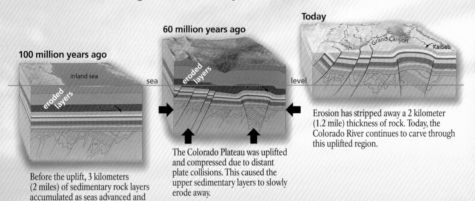

100 million years ago

inland sea

sea

eroded layers

Kaibab

Before the uplift, 3 kilometers (2 miles) of sedimentary rock layers accumulated as seas advanced and retreated many times.

60 million years ago

eroded layers

Kaibab

The Colorado Plateau was uplifted and compressed due to distant plate collisions. This caused the upper sedimentary layers to slowly erode away.

Today

level

Grand Canyon

Kaibab

Erosion has stripped away a 2 kilometer (1.2 mile) thickness of rock. Today, the Colorado River continues to carve through this uplifted region.

Imagine the rocks that used to be here.

eroded layers

Kaibab (KYE-bab)

Tapeats

Layers containing dinosaur fossils have been removed by erosion.

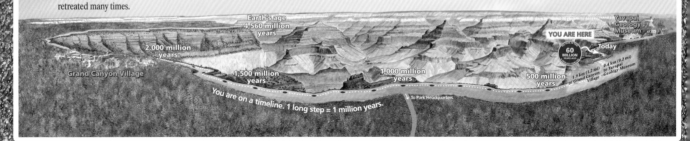

Earth's age 4,560 million years

Yavapai Geology Museum

2,000 million years

YOU ARE HERE

Today

60 MILLION YEARS AGO

Grand Canyon Village

1,500 million years

1,000 million years

500 million years

1.9 km (1.2 mi) to Grand Canyon Village

0.4 km (0.2 mi) to Yavapai Geology Museum

You are on a timeline. 1 long step = 1 million years.

To Park Headquarters

Uplift of the Colorado Plateau took place in three stages and continues today.[2]

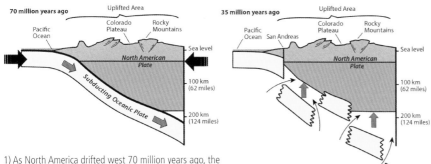

70 million years ago

Uplifted Area — Colorado Plateau, Rocky Mountains

Pacific Ocean

North American Plate

Sea level

100 km (62 miles)

200 km (124 miles)

Subducting Oceanic Plate

1) As North America drifted west 70 million years ago, the tectonic plate forming the floor of the Pacific Ocean pushed east. As the oceanic plate dove below the continent, it squeezed the continent and both the Rocky Mountains and the Colorado Plateau began rising (the Laramide orogeny).

35 million years ago

Uplifted Area — Colorado Plateau, Rocky Mountains

Pacific Ocean   San Andreas

North American Plate

Sea level

100 km (62 miles)

200 km (124 miles)

2) North America began rising again about 35 million years ago. A cold slab of oceanic crust (formerly the floor of the Pacific) fell away deeper into Earth's hot mantle allowing hot, buoyant rock from the mantle to replace it. This triggered explosive volcanic eruptions in the western United States.

How do you cut a layer cake at home? One way is to bring your cake knife down through the layers. Another way is to hold the knife still and lift the cake up through the knife. The river is like the knife and the land is like the cake.

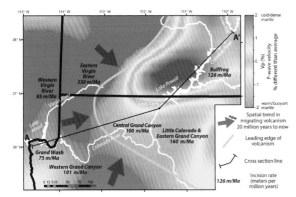

Geophysical image of today's mantle velocity structure at 80 km depth.[23,28]

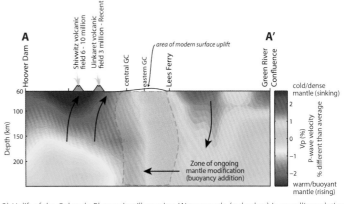

3) Uplift of the Colorado Plateau is still ongoing. Warm mantle (red colors) is upwelling relative to cold zones (blue). This is causing volcanism, faulting, and surface warping.[23,28, 29]

Know your Temples: The view from Grandeur Point on the Trail of Time.

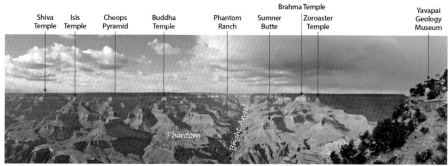

Shiva Temple · Isis Temple · Cheops Pyramid · Buddha Temple · Phantom Ranch · Sumner Butte · Brahma Temple · Zoroaster Temple · Yavapai Geology Museum

Phantom · Bright Angel

Panoramic view looking north from the Trail of Time near Yavapai Museum. Can you identify the different temples and towers? Phantom Ranch? Bright Angel Creek?

Coconino Sandstone
Hermit Shale
Supai Group

Zoroaster Temple was described by George Wharton James in 1902 as "a pillar of fire;" he named it for a Persian religious leader. The white cliffs are the Coconino Sandstone.

Bright Angel fault

Kaibab
Toroweap
150 feet higher
Coconino
Hermit
Supai
Group

The view towards the west from near Grandeur Point reveals a bird's eye view of the Bright Angel Trail. Can you spot people and mules on the trail? This trail follows a natural break in the cliffs that was also used for millennia by Native Americans. In 1891 pioneers improved it to reach mining claims and in 1928 the trail was taken over by the Park. This break is caused by the Bright Angel fault; can you see how the west side was lifted about 46 meters (150 feet) higher than the east side by movement on the fault? If you walk the Early Earth Trail on the other side of the Village, you have to ascend the fault in one semi-steep portion of the Trail of Time.

What a view you get from Grandeur Point near marker 140.

140 Ma

The top layer is 270 million years old.

The horizontal layers were deposited as sediments, over millions of years. Each layer covered the one below. Time, pressure, and burial turned them into sedimentary rocks.

See the top layers.

Kaibab
Toroweap
Coconino
Hermit
Esplanade
Wescogame
Manakacha
Watahomigi
Redwall
Muav
Bright Angel
Tapeats

Supai Group

Tonto Group

Shallow sea deposits
River and sea deposits
Sand dune deposits
River deposits

Find the top four layers.

Kaibab (KYE-bab) Formation 270 million years old
Toroweap (TORO-weep) Formation 273 million years old
Coconino (coco-NEE-no) Sandstone 275 million years old
Hermit Formation 280 million years old

Find the fossils.

270 million years ago, this region was a tropical sea. These are the remains of animals that lived in the sea and became fossilized in the Kaibab (KYE-bab) Limestone.

Earth's age 4,560 million years

2,000 million years

Grand Canyon Village

1,500 million years

1,000 million years

500 million years

YOU ARE HERE

270 MILLION YEARS AGO

You are on a timeline. 1 long step = 1 million years.

To Park Headquarters

1.7 km (1.1 mi) to Grand Canyon Village   0.6 km (0.4 mi) to Yavapai Geology Museum

Yavapai Geology Museum

Where in the rock record?

270 MILLION YEARS AGO

270
525
1,200
1,840
million years ago

270
Ma

Aubrey Group records coastal areas and shallow seas of the Permian Period.

The Aubrey Group, the top three layers, records coastal dunes (Coconino), changing shorelines (Toroweap), and a shallow sea (Kaibab). These layers record the advance of a Permian sea across this region.

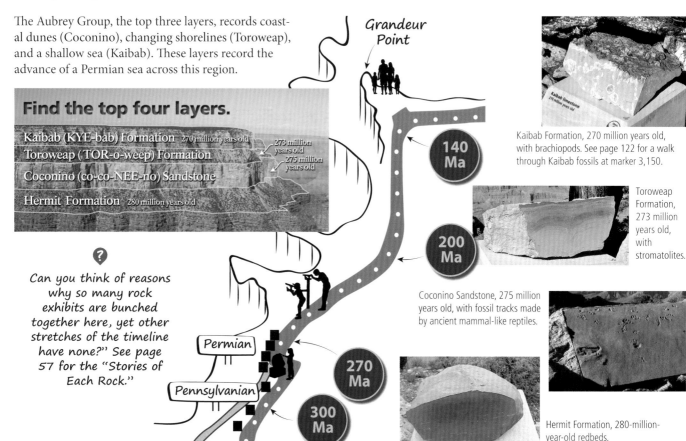

Grandeur Point

Find the top four layers.

Kaibab (KYE-bab) Formation 270 million years old
Toroweap (TOR-o-weep) Formation
Coconino (co-co-NEE-no) Sandstone
Hermit Formation 280 million years old

273 million years old
275 million years old

?

Can you think of reasons why so many rock exhibits are bunched together here, yet other stretches of the timeline have none?" See page 57 for the "Stories of Each Rock."

140 Ma

200 Ma

270 Ma

300 Ma

Permian

Pennsylvanian

Kaibab Formation, 270 million years old, with brachiopods. See page 122 for a walk through Kaibab fossils at marker 3,150.

Kaibab limestone

Toroweap Formation, 273 million years old, with stromatolites.

Coconino Sandstone, 275 million years old, with fossil tracks made by ancient mammal-like reptiles.

Hermit Formation, 280-million-year-old redbeds.

Supai Group records sediments eroded from distant mountains in the Pennsylvanian and Permian Periods.

Supai Group

Esplanade Sandstone, 285 million years old.

Watahomogi Formation, 295 million years old.

See if you can spot Zoroaster Temple and identify the Supai Group below it.

Manakacha Formation, 305 million years old.

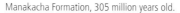

Wescogame Formation, 315 million years old.

Mississippian tropical seas and limestone caves.

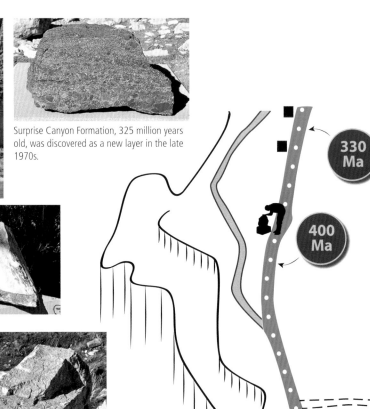

Surprise Canyon Formation, 325 million years old, was discovered as a new layer in the late 1970s.

Redwall Limestone, 340 million years old.

This Redwall sample was installed incorrectly. How would you have installed it to make the bedding horizontal?

Temple Butte Formation is thin to non-existent to the east, then makes its appearance as tidal channels in Marble Canyon, then thickens to become a major limestone cliff in western Grand Canyon.

Temple Butte limestone, 385 million years old.

330 Ma

400 Ma

Tonto Group — flooding of the continent in the Cambrian Period.

The Tonto Group records rapid flooding of North America between 510 and 500 million years ago; this is called a marine transgression.

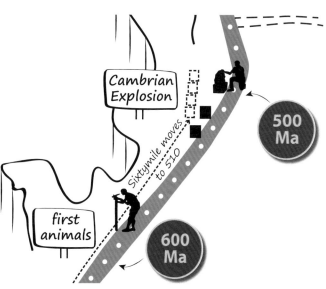

Muav limestone, now dates as 504 million years old.

Tapeats Sandstone, its new maximum age is 508 million years old.

Tapeats was installed incorrectly, bedding should be horizontal.

Bright Angel shale, now dated as 504 million years old.
This sample is upside down (on purpose) to show these trilobite tracks and worm burrows that formed on the bottom of the bed.

Sixtymile Formation, new detrital zircon dates range from 530 to 509 million years old.[30]

Animal life appeared about 630 million years ago.

Sedimentary rock layers at Grand Canyon, as elsewhere on Earth, record an "explosion" in the diversity of animal life.

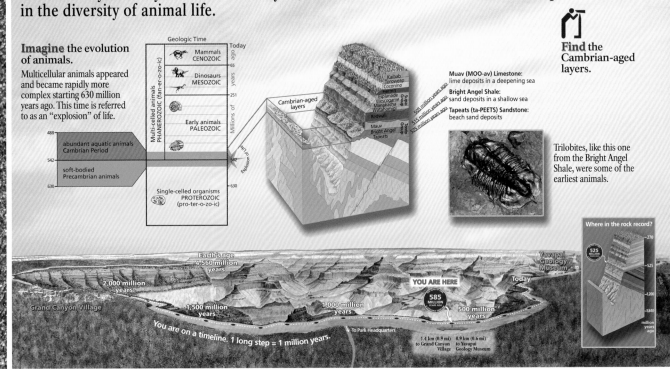

Imagine the evolution of animals.

Multicellular animals appeared and became rapidly more complex starting 630 million years ago. This time is referred to as an "explosion" of life.

Geologic Time

		Today
Multi-celled animals PHANEROZOIC (fan-er-o-zo-ic)	Mammals CENOZOIC	
	Dinosaurs MESOZOIC	65
		251
	Early animals PALEOZOIC	

488
abundant aquatic animals
Cambrian Period
542

542

soft-bodied
Precambrian animals
630

630

Single-celled organisms
PROTEROZOIC
(pro-ter-o-zo-ic)

Millions of years ago

Cambrian-aged layers

Kaibab
Toroweap
Coconino
Hermit
Esplanade
Wescogame
Manakacha
Watahomigi
Redwall
Muav
Bright Angel
Tapeats

Supai Group

Tonto Group

505 million years ago
515 million years ago
525 million years ago

Find the Cambrian-aged layers.

Muav (MOO-av) Limestone: lime deposits in a deepening sea

Bright Angel Shale: sand deposits in a shallow sea

Tapeats (ta-PEETS) Sandstone: beach sand deposits

Trilobites, like this one from the Bright Angel Shale, were some of the earliest animals.

Earth's age
4,560 million
years

2,000 million
years

Grand Canyon Village

1,500 million
years

1,000 million
years

YOU ARE HERE

585
MILLION
YEARS AGO

500 million
years

Today

Yavapai
Geology
Museum

Where in the rock record?

525
MILLION
YEARS AGO

~270
~525
~1,200
~1,840
million
years
ago

You are on a timeline. 1 long step = 1 million years.

To Park Headquarters

1.4 km (0.9 mi)
to Grand Canyon
Village

0.9 km (0.6 mi)
to Yavapai
Geology Museum

585
Ma

Chuar Group was deposited 775 to 729 million years ago in 3 formations and 8 mappable units.[17]

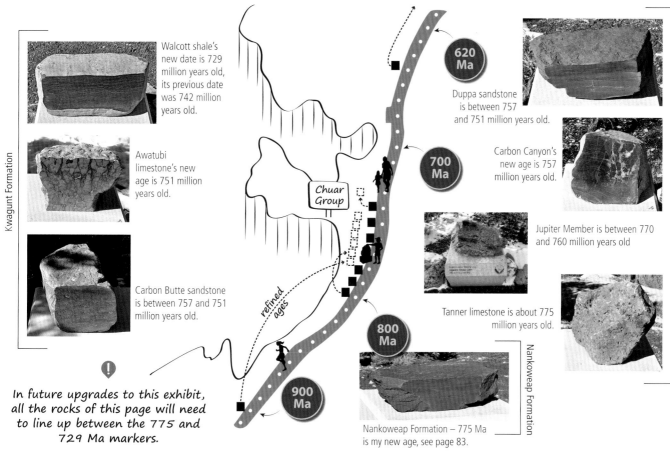

Kwagunt Formation

Walcott shale's new date is 729 million years old, its previous date was 742 million years old.

Awatubi limestone's new age is 751 million years old.

Carbon Butte sandstone is between 757 and 751 million years old.

refined ages

Chuar Group

620 Ma

700 Ma

800 Ma

900 Ma

Duppa sandstone is between 757 and 751 million years old.

Carbon Canyon's new age is 757 million years old.

Jupiter Member is between 770 and 760 million years old

Tanner limestone is about 775 million years old.

Nankoweap Formation – 775 Ma is my new age, see page 83.

Nankoweap Formation

Galeros Formation

Main Trail of Time

In future upgrades to this exhibit, all the rocks of this page will need to line up between the 775 and 729 Ma markers.

The Chuar Group,[17] 775 to 729 million years old, is famous for diverse single-celled microfossils, its record of rifting of Rodinia, and climate changes leading into the time of the Snowball Earth.

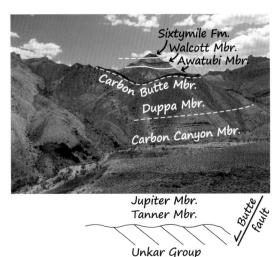

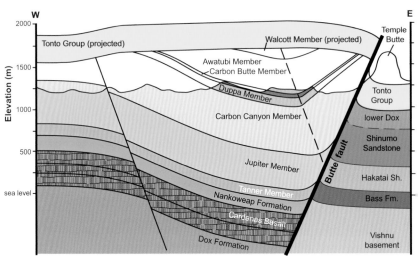

The 775 to 729-million-year-old Chuar Group is exposed only in eastern Grand Canyon. It is about 2 km thick, with the upper half shown here. It consists of shallow marine mudstones and dolostones. These rocks contain diverse single-celled microfossils including the first heterotrophic organisms that lived on Earth (see pages 76-77). The rocks record dramatic swings in climate that pre-dated but may have led into the first Snowball Earth global glaciation 717 million years ago.

In E-W cross section, the Chuar Group is folded and faulted by the Butte fault. The fault was slipping (west-side-DOWN) to form the Chuar sedimentary basin during rifting of the continent. There is NO Chuar Group east of the Butte fault, only the Unkar Group. The Cambrian Tonto Group is not folded by the Chuar syncline, but is faulted with the opposite offset (west-side-UP) showing that the Butte fault was reactivated during Laramide compression about 70 million years ago. This fault slipped multiple times!

Headquarters Trail portal — find the Grand Canyon Supergroup seating rocks.

A side trail from the Park Headquarters area reaches the rim near the 1,000 year marker. It is marked with a two-sided portal so if you are entering or exiting at this point, you have the information you need.

Walking north onto the Trail.

Walking south toward Park Headquarters.

Ripple Marks in the Bass Formation.

The bottom surface of the "Golf Ball bed" of the Cambrian Sixtymile Formation has these circular structures of unknown origin.

The "Brain Bed" (Boxonia) stromatolites from the Chuar Group are fossilized colonies of blue-green algae.

1,010 Ma

MORE ON THIS TOPIC

1.2 billion years is missing from the rock record.

Gaps in the rock record are called unconformities. They represent times when rocks were eroded from the rock record, like chapters torn from a book.

Imagine how gaps in the rock record form.

See the Great Unconformity.

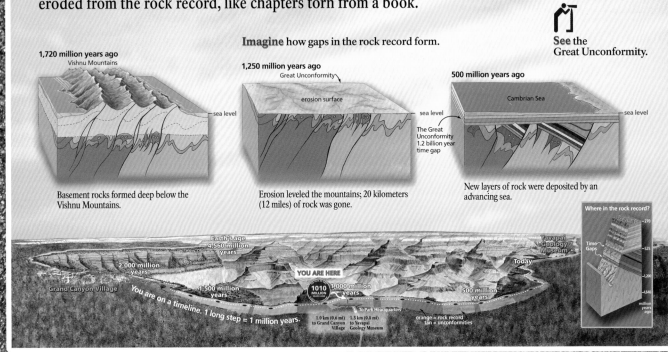

1,720 million years ago
Vishnu Mountains

sea level

Basement rocks formed deep below the Vishnu Mountains.

1,250 million years ago
Great Unconformity

erosion surface

sea level

The Great Unconformity 1.2 billion year time gap

Erosion leveled the mountains; 20 kilometers (12 miles) of rock was gone.

500 million years ago

Cambrian Sea

sea level

New layers of rock were deposited by an advancing sea.

Earth's age 4,560 million years

Yavapai Geology Museum

2,000 million years

Grand Canyon Village

1,500 million years

YOU ARE HERE

1010 MILLION YEARS AGO

1,000 million years

Today

500 million years

You are on a timeline. 1 long step = 1 million years.

To Park Headquarters

1.0 km (0.6 mi) to Grand Canyon Village

1.3 km (0.8 mi) to Yavapai Geology Museum

orange = rock record
tan = unconformities

Where in the rock record?

270
525
1,200
1,840
million years ago

Time Gaps

Add up Grand Canyon's Great Unconformities.

Four unconformities add up to make the Great Unconformity[31]; each represents a period of erosion. In round numbers, from the bottom: 1) Unkar Group (1,250 million) on top of basement (1,750 million) represents erosion and unroofing of the Vishnu Mountains and 500 million years missing at this nonconformity. 2) There is an disconformity of 100 million years within Unkar Group. 3) Chuar Group (800 million) was deposited on upper Unkar Group (1,100 million) with an angular unconformity that represents 300 million years missing because of erosion. 4) Sixtymile Formation (530 million) deposited on upper Chuar Group (730 million) represents 200 million years missing. Add the duration of Unkar (100 million) and Chaur (50 million) deposition to equal 1,250 million years of time missing in locations where the Tonto Group (510 million) rests directly on basement (1,750 million) and 1.3 billion years in places where the Tonto Group rests on Elves Chasm gneiss. That's a lot of time gaps. If you add the 150 million year disconformity in the Paleozoic rocks, and the erosion of the Mesozoic and Cenozoic strata, that makes about 80% of the past 2 billion years of time that is missing (not recorded) at Grand Canyon, yet it is still one of the world's best rock records!

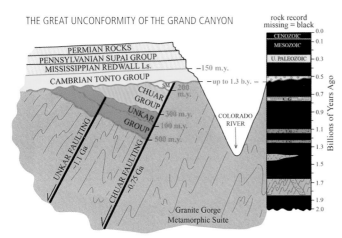

THE GREAT UNCONFORMITY OF THE GRAND CANYON

Unconformities are rock contacts where rocks below and above are separated by a time gap. Time went by, but there are no rocks at that spot to record it.

In this view from Lipan Point in eastern Grand Canyon, flat-lying Tonto Group (510 Ma) rests on tilted Unkar Group (1,255–1,100 Ma). There is up to 750 million years of history missing here. This is called an angular unconformity because the Unkar Group was tilted and eroded before the Tonto Group was deposited.

Main Trail of Time

The tilted layers are the Grand Canyon Supergroup.

These sedimentary layers were deposited and then tilted 1,200 to 740 million years ago.

See the Supergroup rocks.

Supergroup Rocks

Shinumo
Hakatai
Bass

Visualize how the Supergroup rocks formed.

1,100 million years ago
pull-apart (rift) basins
sea level

The lower Supergroup was deposited in rift basins that pulled apart.

740 million years ago
Chuar Sea
sea level
Upper Grand Canyon Supergroup
Lower Grand Canyon Supergroup

The lower Supergroup was tilted as the upper Supergroup was deposited.

530 million years ago
sandstone ridges
sea level

Erosion produced a nearly flat continent.

Only single-celled life existed.

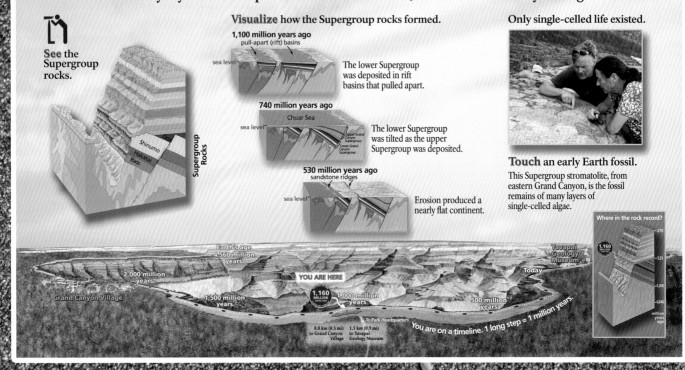

Touch an early Earth fossil.

This Supergroup stromatolite, from eastern Grand Canyon, is the fossil remains of many layers of single-celled algae.

Earth's age 4,560 million years

2,000 million years

Grand Canyon Village

1,500 million years

YOU ARE HERE

1,160 MILLION YEARS AGO

1,000 million years

500 million years

Today

Yavapai Geology Museum

0.8 km (0.5 mi) to Grand Canyon Village

1.5 km (0.9 mi) to Yavapai Geology Museum

To Park Headquarters

You are on a timeline. 1 long step = 1 million years.

Where in the rock record?

1,160 MILLION YEARS AGO

270
525
1,200
1,040
million years ago

The Unkar Group,[16] 1,255 to 1,100 million years old, contains Grand Canyon's oldest fossils. It is over 2 km thick as measured from these tilted strata beneath the Great Angular Unconformity.

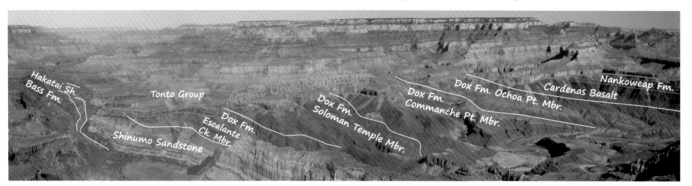

The Unkar Group can be seen in its full thickness from Lipan Point in eastern Grand Canyon as shown above. When you take out the tilt, as at the right, it is over 2 km thick! It was deposited in subsiding basins on top of deeply exhumed basement rocks. The deep erosion along the Great Nonconformity, the subsidence of Unkar basins, and faulting took place as the continent was colliding with another continental mass in the region that is now Texas. Grand Canyon's oldest fossils, 1.25 billion year old stromatolites, formed from algal colonies in a shallow sea.

Grand Canyon Supergroup: new dating now puts Sixtymile Formation in the Cambrian Tonto Group and the Nankoweap Formation in the Chuar Group.

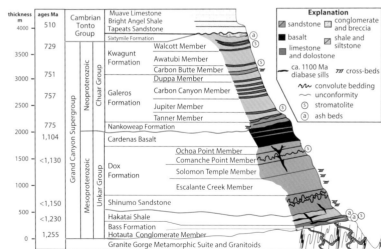

Unkar Group — 1,255 to 1,100 Ma sedimentary rocks record assembly of an early supercontinent.[16]

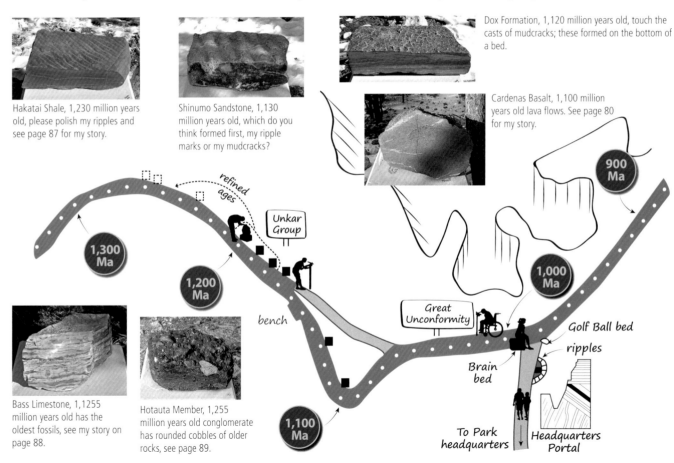

Hakatai Shale, 1,230 million years old, please polish my ripples and see page 87 for my story.

Shinumo Sandstone, 1,130 million years old, which do you think formed first, my ripple marks or my mudcracks?

Dox Formation, 1,120 million years old, touch the casts of mudcracks; these formed on the bottom of a bed.

Cardenas Basalt, 1,100 million years old lava flows. See page 80 for my story.

Bass Limestone, 1,1255 million years old has the oldest fossils, see my story on page 88.

Hotauta Member, 1,255 million years old conglomerate has rounded cobbles of older rocks, see page 89.

refined ages

Unkar Group

bench

Great Unconformity

Golf Ball bed

ripples

Brain bed

To Park headquarters

Headquarters Portal

1,300 Ma

1,200 Ma

1,100 Ma

1,000 Ma

900 Ma

Stretches along the Trail of Time with few rock exhibits encode the unconformities.

The juniper tree offers a Deep Time Intermission

Step back from Deep Time (near the 1,370 million year marker).

Q. Is this juniper tree alive or dead?
A. As of 2018 it had a small live branch — see if it is still there when you visit?

Q. How old is this tree?
A. About 800 years (not million years) old.

Q. How do we know?
A. A Park Ranger drilled a tiny hole in the tree with a special tool and counted its rings.

Q. Where would it fit on the Trail of Time?
A. It would fit on the Million Year Trail at the 800-years-ago marker.

Q. Were people in the Grand Canyon then?
A. Yes, the Ancestral Puebloan peoples lived and farmed in Grand Canyon 800 years ago!

1,375 million-year-old Quartermaster granite is a loner found in western Grand Canyon; it fills one spot along the Great Unconformity stretch.

1,300 Ma

1,400 Ma

1,500 Ma

1,600 Ma

The long stretches that have no rock exhibits (or just one) represent long periods of erosion that left gaps (unconformities) in the rock record.

MORE ON THIS TOPIC ▶

Vishnu rocks are near the canyon's bottom.

Vishnu basement rocks formed 1,750 to 1,660 million years ago. They tell the story of how Earth's continental crust formed in this region.

Imagine how the basement rocks formed.

See Vishnu rocks.

Touch the basement rocks.

1,750 million years ago
volcanic island chains

magma

→Compression←

1,720 million years ago
Vishnu Mountains

The basement rocks formed as Earth's plates collided and island chains were welded together.

Sedimentary rocks form when sediments are buried and harden into rock.

Igneous rocks form when lava and magma cool and become solid.

In metamorphic rocks, new minerals grow due to heat and pressure.

basement rocks

Heat and pressure caused the basement rocks to fold and flow. You can see these folds in this rock!

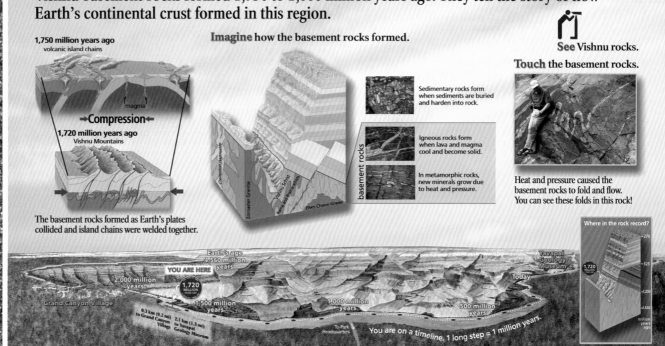

Earth's age 4,560 million years

YOU ARE HERE

2,000 million years

1,720 MILLION YEARS AGO

1,500 million years

1,000 million years

500 million years

Today

Yavapai Geology Museum

Grand Canyon Village

0.3 km (0.2 mi) to Grand Canyon Village

2.1 km (1.3 mi) to Yavapai Geology Museum

To Park Headquarters

You are on a timeline. 1 long step = 1 million years.

Where in the rock record?

1,720 Ma

Vishnu basement rocks tell us about deep earth processes of flow and metamorphism. These rocks formed at the surface, were buried to 20-km depths and folded in the Vishnu Mountains, and are now back at the surface.

Rama, Brahma, and Vishnu schists formed in volcanic arcs and arc-related sedimentary basins and were folded together in the deep crust during plate collisions about 1.7 billion years ago.

Granite Gorge Metamorphic Suite includes the metavolcanic and metasedimentary rocks.[32]

Rama Schist, 1,755 million years old.

Brama Schist, 1,755 million years old.

Vishnu Schist, 1,745 million years old.

About half of the basement rocks formed when magmas cooled deep in the Earth.[18]

The older set of magmas, the granodiorites, formed from mantle melting in subduction settings.

Zoroaster pluton, 1,740 million years old.

Diamond Creek pluton, 1,736 million years old.

Trinity pluton, 1,730 million years old.

Ruby pluton, 1,716 million years old.

Horn pluton, 1,713 million years old.

The younger set of magmas, the granites and pegmatites, formed from deep crustal melting.

Cremation pegmatite, 1,698 million years old.

Grand Canyon Village

El Tovar parking

Verkamps History Museum

Verkamps Portal

Road to El Tovar

2,000 Ma

1,900 Ma

1,800 Ma

oldest rock

Vishnu basement

1,840 Ma

1,700 Ma

1,650 Ma

Elves Chasm gneiss, 1,840 million years old (1.84 billion) is a bit of a loner in recording Grand Canyon's earliest basement.[32]

Phantom pluton, 1,662 million years old.

Grand Canyon's rocks are incredibly old.

Grand Canyon's oldest known rock is called the Elves Chasm Gneiss (pronounced "NICE") and it is 1,840 million years old.

Maricopa Point

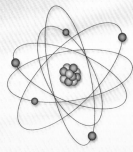

Imagine how old?

The 1,840 million year old Elves Chasm Gneiss is almost unimaginably old, yet it is only 2/5 the age of the Earth. To reach the 4,560 million year age of the Earth along the Trail of Time, walk west 2.7 kilometers (1.7 miles), to Maricopa Point.

How do we know?

Geologists can tell how old a rock is by counting the atoms produced by natural radioactive decay.

Touch a rock that is 1,840 million years old.

This rock sample came from the bottom of the canyon 32 kilometers (20 miles) west of here.

This rock was first formed as granite when magma cooled 1,840 million years ago. Pressure and heat then changed it into gneiss (pronounced NICE) about 1,700 million years ago.

YOU ARE HERE

Earth's age 4,560 million years

2,000 million years

1,840 MILLION YEARS AGO

Grand Canyon Village

0.2 km (0.1 mi) to Grand Canyon Village

2.2 km (1.3 mi) to Yavapai Geology Museum

1,500 million years

1,000 million years

To Park Headquarters

500 million years

Today

Yavapai Geology Museum

You are on a timeline, 1 long step = 1 million years.

Where in the rock record?

1,840 MILLION YEARS AGO

270

525

1,200

1,840 million years ago

Main Trail of Time

The Village Portal – 2 billion years of Earth's history.

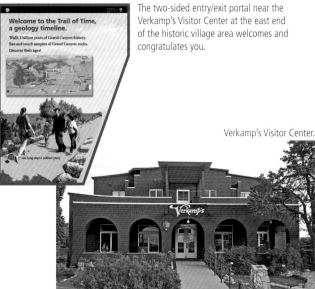

The two-sided entry/exit portal near the Verkamp's Visitor Center at the east end of the historic village area welcomes and congratulates you.

Verkamp's Visitor Center.

The Village portal has pavers of basement rock and seating rocks of pegmatite, schist and gneiss.

Missing commas? Our evaluations indicated that numbers with commas would be more easily understood, but the fabricator didn't cast them in! The set of markers above is especially prone to confusion because these numbers look like recent years on the human calendar rather than the last 5 million-year-steps on the Main segment of the Trail of Time.

Historic Grand Canyon Village.

Age of the Earth at Maricopa Point ←

Muav Ls.

Bright Angel Sh.

Tapeats Ss.

Shinumo Ss.

Hakatai Sh.

Bass Fm.

basement

The Trail of Time is not marked through the busy Historic Village area, but picks up again at the west end of the Village near the Hermits Rest shuttle bus stop. The village area includes the 1905 El Tovar Hotel, 1905 Hopi House, and 1935 Bright Angel Lodge. The stone wall along the canyon rim path was built by workers from the Civilian Conservation Corps in the 1930s. En route between the Main Trail and the Early Earth Trail, stop in at Bright Angel Lodge and visit the fireplace that shows the rock layers (below left).

Mary Colter designed Hopi House as well as the geologic fireplace in Bright Angel Lodge that uses the real rocks from Grand Canyon and shows the 3 sets of rocks plus accurate details of the Tapeats and Bright Angel onlapping monadnocks (Cambrian islands) of Shinumo Sandstone shown by the white line. River cobbles at the base are a nice touch symbolizing that a young river carved through the very old rock layers. This was advanced and nuanced geologic interpretation in the 1930s and remains so today.

El Tovar Hotel (above), and Hopi House (below) are historic buildings in the village area near the 2,000-million-year marker on the Main Trail of Time.

Imagine a time before the canyon's oldest rocks formed.

Some of Grand Canyon's oldest rocks contain fragments of still older rocks.

Imagine looking inside the Vishnu Schist.

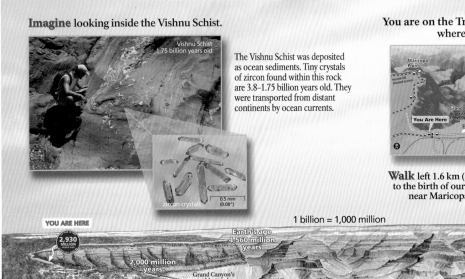

Vishnu Schist
1.75 billion years old

The Vishnu Schist was deposited as ocean sediments. Tiny crystals of zircon found within this rock are 3.8–1.75 billion years old. They were transported from distant continents by ocean currents.

zircon crystals

0.5 mm (0.08")

You are on the Trail of Time, a geology timeline trail where 1 meter = 1 million years.

Yavapai Geology Museum

Maricopa Point

Trail of Time

Grand Canyon Village

You Are Here

Amphitheater

Park Headquarters

Shrine of the Ages

Verkamps Visitor Center

Bright Angel Lodge

Train Depot

Market Plaza

Parking Lot

Shuttle Bus Stop

Bathroom

Walk left 1.6 km (1.0 mi) to the birth of our planet near Maricopa Point

Walk right 1.1 km (0.7 mi) to Grand Canyon's oldest rocks, just past Grand Canyon Village.

1 billion = 1,000 million

YOU ARE HERE

2,930 MILLION YEARS AGO

Earth's age 4,560 million years

2,000 million years

Grand Canyon's oldest rocks

1,500 million years

Grand Canyon Village

1,000 million years

500 million years

Yavapai Geology Museum

Today

You are on a timeline. 1 long step = 1 million years.

To Park Headquarters

THE EARLY EARTH TRAIL

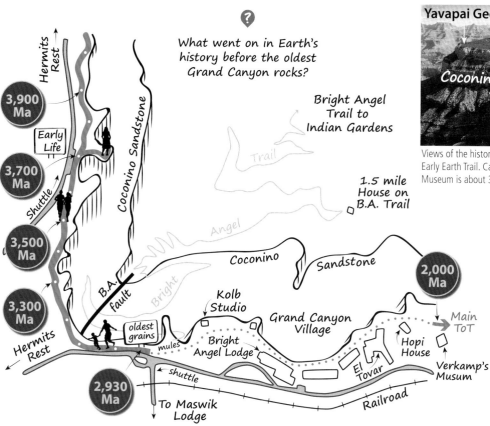

What went on in Earth's history before the oldest Grand Canyon rocks?

Yavapai Geology Museum

Coconino Ss.

El Tovar

Views of the historic Grand Canyon Village are spectacular from the Early Earth Trail. Can you spot the top of El Tovar? Yavapai Geology Museum is about 3 kilometers (3 billion years) in the distance.

Bright Angel Trail to Indian Gardens

1.5 mile House on B.A. Trail

The Early Earth segment of the Trail of Time is marked from the Hermit Transfer shuttle bus stop at the far west end of the historic village area and continues north to Maricopa Point. This steeper section of trail is not as heavily-visited as the Main segment. Numbered bronze trail markers designate the timeline every 10 meters. Four wayside panels highlight this 1.6 km (1.0 mile) segment. All of the Grand Canyon's rocks came later than this section of the timeline.

Life appeared when Earth was still a young planet.

Earth's earliest history is not recorded by rocks at Grand Canyon, but is known from rocks found elsewhere around the world.

Find Earth's oldest rocks.

The oldest known rocks on Earth are 4 billion years old, more than twice as old as Grand Canyon's oldest known rocks.

Imagine a world with *only* single-celled life.

Modern stromatolites growing in water

3.45 billion-year-old stromatolites preserved in rock

Earth's oldest known fossils are 3.8 billion years old. They formed in algal mounds and are called stromatolites. They helped to slowly oxygenate the planet.

You are on the Trail of Time, a geology timeline trail where 1 meter = 1 million years.

Walk left 0.9 km (0.5 mi) to the birth of our planet near Maricopa Point

Walk right 1.9 km (1.2 mi) to Grand Canyon's oldest rocks, just past Grand Canyon Village.

YOU ARE HERE

3,700 MILLION YEARS AGO

1 billion = 1,000 million

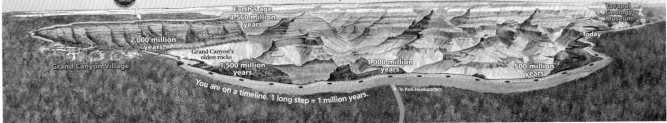

Earth's age 4,560 million years

2,000 million years

Grand Canyon Village

Grand Canyon's oldest rocks 1,500 million years

You are on a timeline. 1 long step = 1 million years.

To Park Headquarters

1,000 million years

500 million years

Today

Yavapai Geology Museum

The time from 4,000 to 4,600 million years ago was the time of early bombardment and Earth formation.

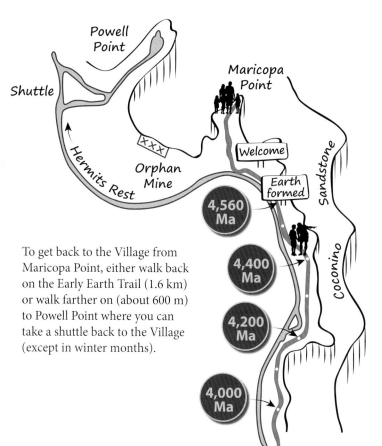

To get back to the Village from Maricopa Point, either walk back on the Early Earth Trail (1.6 km) or walk farther on (about 600 m) to Powell Point where you can take a shuttle back to the Village (except in winter months).

Since the Early Earth segment has many entry points, each of the welcome waysides gives an introduction to the Trail of Time. Each panel includes the "You are on the Trail of Time" explanation and map for those who are encountering the Trail for the first time. Each panel also adds some new information to the Earth story. A fitting rock for the age of the Earth end of the Trail of Time would be a meteorite such as the Diablo Canyon meteorite that made Meteor Crater. The earliest history of the Earth involved such intense meteorite bombardment that Earth's crust was continually remelted and reworked. Because of this, the oldest rocks found on Earth that are FROM Earth are about 4 billion years old. The OLDEST rocks ON Earth came from the solar system in the form of meteorites. From dating of meteorites, we know the 4.56 billion-year-old age of the Earth and solar system.

Sample of Canyon Diablo Meteorite, an iron meteorite that formed in the solar system 4.56 billion years ago and fell to Earth 50,000 years ago to form Arizona's Meteor Crater.

Earth formed 4,560 million years ago.

You can feel how incredibly old the Earth is by walking the Trail of Time. To walk the whole trail takes 4,560 long steps.

Visualize swirling dust.

Earth and our solar system formed 4,560 billion years ago from a spinning nebular cloud of dust and rock.

Where are Earth's oldest rocks?

The oldest rocks found on Earth are 4.56 billion-year-old meteorites that impacted the Earth.

Meteor Crater, Arizona

You are on the Trail of Time, a geology timeline trail where 1 meter = 1 million years.

Walk right 2.7 km (1.7 mi) to Grand Canyon's oldest rocks, just past Grand Canyon Village.

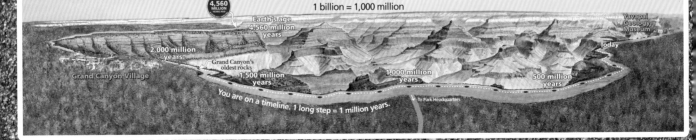

YOU ARE HERE

4,560 MILLION YEARS AGO

1 billion = 1,000 million

Earth's age 4,560 million years

2,000 million years

Grand Canyon's oldest rocks 1,500 million years

Grand Canyon Village

1,000 million years

500 million years

Today

Yavapai Geology Museum

You are on a timeline. 1 long step = 1 million years.

To Park Headquarters

Welcome to the Trail of Time, a geology timeline.

Walk south along this path to the start of the Trail of Time, a giant geologic timeline where 1 meter = 1 million years.

Find the 4.56 billion year age of the Earth about 200 m (220 yards) ahead.

Ponder Earth's history as you walk from the formation of our planet, through Grand Canyon's rock record, to Today.

YOU ARE HERE

1 billion = 1,000 million

Earth's age 4,560 million years

2,000 million years

Grand Canyon's oldest rocks 1,500 million years

Grand Canyon Village

1,000 million years

500 million years

Today

Yavapai Geology Museum

You are on a timeline. 1 long step = 1 million years.

To Park Headquarters

The age of the Universe — the Big Bang marker at Pima Point.

Pima Point has a marker for the age of the Universe

2000 MARKER

Grand Canyon Village

Maricopa Point 4,560 MARKER

Yavapai Geology Museum, Today MARKER

The sciences of astronomy, physics, and biology, as well as geology, all continue to refine our understanding of the age of the Universe, the Solar System, the Earth, and the earliest life. The time of the Big Bang origin of our still-expanding universe is dated by astronomers to be 13.75 billion years ago. This marker is OUT THERE, at Pima Point; its position was measured approximately (on maps) following the rim using the Trail of Time scale of 1 meter = 1 million years. The universe is 9.2 billion years older than the Earth.

THE TRAIL OF TIME
13,750 MILLION YEARS AGO
A GEOLOGY TIMELINE

STORIES FROM GRAND CANYON'S ROCKS (told by the rocks themselves).

Geologists name rock units from nearby places, which often themselves got named in colorful ways.[33] You can think of the individual rocks as the historians that record information from their time and their layer. For the Trail of Time labeling we decided to use rock-type names on the plinth rather than their formal layer names. This chapter can help you also learn these "family" names. Several similar rock layers can form a member (like a family), several members make up a formation (like a big family), formations are often part of a group (like an extended family), and groups combine into supergroups.

The age of each rock as placed along the Trail of Time was determined from the best evidence we had in 2009. Igneous rocks crystallize (freeze) quickly (in much less than one million years) and are dated by uranium-lead radiometric methods mainly using zircon crystals. These dates have plus or minus error bars giving precision of the analysis (for example 1840 ± 1 million years for Elves Chasm gneiss). On the other hand, sedimentary layers accumulate over many million years and one can imagine numerous individual samples spread out on the timeline Trail from their top (youngest) to bottom (oldest) layer. Sometimes there are volcanic interlayers that can be directly dated (1,255 + 2 Ma for the Bass Formation and 729 + 0.3 Ma for the Walcott Member of the Kwagunt Formation), but more commonly sedimentary layers are "dated" relative to one another based on superposition (upper layers are younger than lower layers) and based on index fossils that are getting increasingly better dated (globally and locally) from the places that have volcanic layers. New technologies continue to improve dating methods and many rock ages on the Trail of Time have been refined in the past 10 years. In these cases, the rock stories will tell you their updated ages based on the 2018 calibration of the geologic timescale.[34] They hope to be moved to these now-better-known "birthdays" in future improvements of the Trail of Time Exhibit.

Each rock along the Trail of Time has a story to tell. Geologists are detectives who specialize in uncovering the evidence for these stories. The younger rocks have stories that are in sharper focus; the older ones have memory gaps but remember farther back. Like human history and pre-history, the stories are interwoven. Gaps in the rock record (unconformities) represent times when we have no rock layers acting as "historians" here at Grand Canyon. You'll notice these times as long stretches along the Trail of Time with no rocks. But time went on and so do the markers on the timeline. Fortunately, it is often possible for geologists to learn about what went on by visiting other locations that do not have the same gaps in the record.

Each rock's story occurs in the following pages with its picture and age marker number. Other photos on each page help you get to know the natural outcrop setting, artist renditions of what the region might have looked like, or fossils and other features in the story. These are short introductions. References are provided for those who want to dig deeper. Each rock wants you to know its formal name, its rock type (sedimentary, igneous, or metamorphic), its age (and how well it is known), and its story.

Travertines are the youngest rocks, forming today.[35]

Travertine, about 100,000 years old. My banding formed by chemical precipitation, layer by layer; I like to think that my "chemistry rocks!"

I got deposited when naturally carbonated spring waters degassed in turbulent streams like the Little Colorado River (above left) or in "stone waterfalls" like Travertine Falls (above right).

My formal name: I am called Elves Chasm travertine, named for my Elves Chasm mother spring where I formed. I have relatives in Havasu Creek and the Little Colorado River.

My rock type is a sedimentary rock; specifically a chemical sedimentary rock that is entirely made up of calcium carbonate ($CaCO_3$).

My age: My family at Elves Chasm ranges from more than 1 million years old to modern travertines. The ones forming today are some of the youngest rocks in Grand Canyon. Coincidentally, I am named for the same place as some of the Grand Canyon's oldest rock, Elves Chasm gneiss. We get along fine despite our 1.84-billion-year difference in age.

My story: We travertines are freshwater limestones that form from degassing of CO_2 gas that originated in Earth's mantle. Waters that deposited me originated as snowmelt, picked up volcanic CO_2 that was coming up faults from 100-km depths, and flowed through pores, cracks, and caves to my spring vent. The time spent in the limestone caves of the Redwall-Muav aquifer were exciting — my parent waters were chemically aggressive and helped dissolve new caves, deposited stalactites, and also picked up more calcium carbonate from the limestone. When the carbonated groundwater came to the surface, pressure dropped, bubbles left, and I formed as a precipitate, like scale in a teakettle. I built up layer by layer in the stream; thicker layers during past wet times and thinner (or no) layers during dry times so my layering records past climates.

20,000 yrs

"What a conflict of water and fire there must have been here."

Basalt lava rock, about 550,000 years old.

Spectacular fountains of molten rock (this one in Hawaii) spew high into the air and the erupted basalt flows downhill.

Lava flows cascaded into Grand Canyon from volcanoes like Vulcan's throne on the north rim. As John Wesley Powell wrote in 1875: *"What a conflict of water and fire there must have been here! Just imagine a river of molten rock running down into a river of melted snow. What a seething and boiling of the waters; what clouds of steam rolled into the heavens!"[36]*

My formal name: I call myself lava rock. I am from the basalt flows of the Uinkaret volcanic field named for the Paiute word for "place of the pines."

My rock type is an igneous rock, a volcanic breccia as you can see from my angular fragments.

My age is 550,000 years old. Other flows from my volcanic field range from 2.5 million years to a mere 1,000 years old.[37] The ones like me that cascaded into Grand Canyon range in age from 815,000 to 100,000 years old based on Ar-Ar radiometric dating.

My story: I originated from a volcano on the north rim of western Grand Canyon. At about 60 km below Earth's surface my parent magma plucked off pieces of the wallrocks along the crack we were ascending. Check out my brown chunks; these are chunks (xenoliths) of the mantle rock called peridotite. My eruption at the surface was in spectacular fountains of lava spewing high into the air. I had exciting travels on the surface in the weeks following my eruption. I was fragmented like this during the eruption and flowed down the sides of Grand Canyon to its bottom with my cousin basalt flows. Once solidified, we dammed up the Colorado River for a while. But within a thousand years, the lake we created overtopped our dam, the lava dam burst, and the Colorado River carved back through, leaving me as a flow remnant perched above the river channel.

100,000 yrs

Even the hardest rocks get carved, sculpted, and polished by the river.

TOUCH the river-polished rock.

I was sculpted and polished by the powerful Colorado River using its abrasion tools of sand and gravel.

Pebbles swirled around and carved potholes like these. This is one way that the river carves deeper.

My formal name: I represent all the different rock types that get sculpted, smoothed, and polished by the Colorado River.

My rock type is a metamorphic rock; I started out as a basalt and got metamorphosed into an amphibolite, a story you can hear if you walk to marker 1,750 (see page 100).

My age is 1.75 billion years old, but my polish and sculpting took place in the past few hundred thousand years.

My story: I am here at this end of the Trail of Time to tell you about the erosional power of the Colorado River. The billions of years I spent in the deep crust as part of the basement rocks are dim memories to me, but as the river carved the Granite Gorges I ended up right next to the river. I am a very hard rock, but every spring and during summer monsoon floods, the river rose and used its tools of sand and gravel, all banging together, to chip, carve, and polish me into this shape. Some cobbles would swirl around incessantly to carve potholes and these potholes eventually drilled through even the hardest of rocks like me. As you can see and feel, I have been through the "Colorado River finishing school" and am proud to show my fine polish.

6
Ma

Kaibab Limestone[39] of the Aubrey Group is the top layer that forms both rims of Grand Canyon.

Kaibab Formation, 270 million years old. See my gray nodules of chert and turn to page 122 to see more of my fossils.

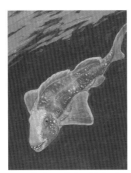

The Kaibab seaway had petalodontid sharks like this one. Artwork by Mary Sundstrom, courtesy of New Mexico Museum of Natural History and Science.

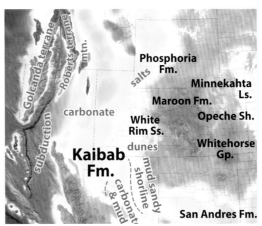

There were open ocean conditions to the northwest and a plate collision going on with oceanic terranes; the shoreline migrated east in lower Kaibab time then west in upper Kaibab time.[38]

My formal name is Kaibab Formation (or sometimes known as Kaibab Limestone) of the Aubrey Group. I am representing both members of the Kaibab Formation: Fossil Mountain Member (my member) and Harrisburg Member (above me). The name Kaibab came from the Paiute words for "mountain lying down," a good description of the Kaibab uplift from which I was named.

My rock type is a sedimentary rock. I am a limestone that formed in an ancient seaway. I have chert nodules made from the silica of sponges. Brachiopods as well as other animals flourished during my time but many species went extinct 252 million years ago.

My age: I am at 270 million years on the Trail of Time; the fossils of the Fossil Mountain Member lived on Earth 269 to 273 million years ago during the Permian Period; Harrisburg Member is probably several million years younger.

My story: I remember when the region was covered by a shallow sea, deeper to the west and the shoreline to the east that migrated back and forth due to changes in sea level. Marine life was abundant and many shells and fragments of animals settled down into my lime mud. After I became a rock (was lithified), my layers were gradually buried deeper over the next 200 million years by a 4 km (2.5 mile) thickness of younger layers, quite a burden. I have been uncovered over the past 70 million years as the region was uplifted and those Mesozoic layers were eroded. I am more resistant than the eroded Mesozoic layers and now I form the rims of Grand Canyon as well as the surrounding Kaibab and Coconino plateaus.

Toroweap Formation:[40] many rock types in one family.

Toroweap Formation, 275 million years old. My layers are a mix of evaporites, mudstone, sandstone, and limestone.

The Permian seaway wasn't as deep as in Kaibab's time, but was deeper than for Coconino's time; shorelines migrated east and west. Cephalopods lived in the Permian seas, as drawn by Mary Sundstrom, courtesy of New Mexico Museum of Natural History and Science.

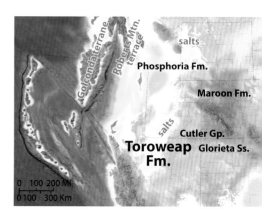

My formal name is Toroweap Formation of the Aubrey Group. I am representing all three members of the Toroweap Formation: Seligman Member (at bottom), Brady Canyon Member (my member), and Woods Ranch Member (above me). The name Toroweap comes from Toroweap Cliffs, named from the Paiute word for "dry gulley" applied by A. H. Thompson, Powell's brother-in-law, in 1872. It was spelled To-ro-wip Cliffs in Powell's 1875 report.

My rock type is a sedimentary rock. I am a limestone with stromatolites (algal structures) as shown by the domes seen on my cut face. The plinth says I am a sandstone but it was labeled that way before my rock was collected because much of my formation is sandstone. When they saw my gorgeous stromatolites, they collected me instead.

My age is 275 million years old; I am at 273 million years on the Trail of Time. My fossils lived 273 to 278 million years ago during the Permian Period.

My story: I was deposited in the same shallow sea as Kaibab Limestone but the shoreline shifted east and west more during my time and left varied rock types in my family. For example, rock layers of salt formed when marine waters evaporated in mudflats, crossbedded sands record advance of coastal sand dunes similar to Coconino, limestones with fossils record deepening of the seaway. My layer is less resistant to erosion than Coconino and Kaibab and hence I now form a slope between their cliffs.

273 Ma

Coconino Sandstone[41] was deposited by strong winds in giant sand dunes.

Coconino Sandstone, 280 million years old. Trackways were made by mammal-like reptiles like this caseasaur. Artwork by Mary Sundstrom, courtesy of New Mexico Museum of Natural History and Science.

wind from NW

bedding

cross bedding

Geologists can tell which way the wind was blowing 280 million years ago! Crossbeds record winds blowing from NW to SE. Visualize the crossbed as the steep face of a huge sand dune moving across the landscape, now preserved as sandstone.

WIND

Lyons Ss.
Maroon Fm.
Organ Rock Sh.
Cutler Gp.
Coconino Sandstone
DeChelly Ss.
Glorieta Ss.
sand sea (erg)
Yeso Fm.
evaporites

0 100 200 Mi
0 100 300 Km

Sand seas called ergs covered the region.

My formal name is Coconino Sandstone of the Aubrey Group. The name Coconino comes from the word "kohonino" that the Hopis used for the Hualapai and Havasupai that they called "people to the west."

My rock type is a sedimentary rock. I am a sandstone, turned into rock from an ancient set of sand dunes.

My age is about 280 million years old based on my position between Hermit and Toroweap.

My story: I was deposited in a vast desert of sand dunes. The Permian sea was still to the northwest. Wind was blowing from the northwest and huge dunes were migrating to the southeast as shown by the steep faces on the downwind side of a dunes called crossbeds that you can see in the cliffs. I had mammal-like reptiles cruising up and down my dunes similar to the lizards that now walk on my rocks. When I turned from sand to sandstone, I was cemented by silica so that I now form resistant cliffs seen as the white "bathtub-ring" that is the third layer down in Grand Canyon. My grains are all similar in size and are frosted from banging together in the wind, like a frosted glass window. I have great porosity and permeability that make me a good aquifer for groundwater flow. And I make nice patios because I break apart into even slabs.

Hermit Formation,[42] the slope former that undermines Coconino.

Hermit Formation, 285 million years old. Feel my sand grains.

At my upper contact, Coconino's windblown sand filtered down deep cracks.

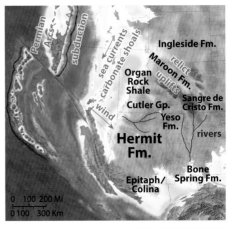

My sediment was deposited as mud in sluggish rivers that flowed towards the Permian seaway west of here. The Ancestral Rockies had been mostly been worn down by erosion.

My formal name is Hermit Formation. I was named for Hermit's Camp on Hermit Trail which was named in 1906. Some think of me as part of the overlying Aubrey Group but I am closer in age to Supai Group below me. Coconino came along several million years after me.

My rock type is a sedimentary rock. Some call me Hermit Shale, but my formation is mainly sandstone and my formal name is Hermit Formation.

My age was placed as 280 million years on the Trail of Time, but 285 million years is my refined age. My fossils lived on Earth between 284 and 290 million years ago during the Permian Period.

My story: I was deposited by sluggish rivers that meandered across a very broad coastal plain with the shoreline west of here. The northwest winds that deposited Esplanade and Coconino were not blowing as much although some dunes found their way into my formation. The time between me and Coconino probably involved a few million years of drying out and large cracks formed that got filled with sand that you can see at my contact with Coconino if you hike down the Bright Angel Trail. I am easy to erode and form a slope in today's canyon. I like to cause trouble by undermining Coconino's cliffs and causing landslides. Groundwater that percolates down through Coconino can't get down past my shale layers and moves sideways into the canyon making springs near our contact.

280 Ma

Esplanade Sandstone of the Supai Group:[42] wind won out over water during my time.

Esplanade Sandstone, 290 million years old. TOUCH the crossbedding on the side.

Esplanade Plateau in western Grand Canyon forms a spectacular bench named by Clarence Dutton. Esplanade Sandstone forms the surface of the wide bench.

Permian Arcs subduction

Tensleep Ss.

Casper Ss.
Weber Ss.

Gothic Ss.

Fountain Ss.

Ancestral Front-range Uncompahgre Uplift

Cedar Mesa Ss.
coastal dunes

Cutler Gp.

Sangre de Cristo Fm.

Esplanade Sandstone

Abo Fm.

Chase Gp.

Pakoon Ls.

Florida Uplift

Hueco Fm.

Earp Fm.

0 100 200 Mi
0 100 300 Km

Dunes had the upper hand relative to the sea in depositing my sands.

My formal name is Esplanade Formation. I am the top and youngest formation of the Supai Group. The name Esplanade was given in 1882 by Clarence Dutton because he likened it to The Esplanade walkway in New York.

My rock type is a sedimentary rock. I am a sandstone with large crossbeds formed by the wind in ancient dunes.

My age: I was placed at 285 million years on the Trail of Time, but 290 million years is my refined age. My fossils lived on Earth in the Permian Period between 290 and 294 million years ago.[42]

My story: I was deposited mainly in coastal sand dunes with the shoreline to the NW of here at about the same time that the Pakoon Limestone was being deposited in the sea to the west of us in Grand Wash cliffs. The Ancestral Rocky Mountains were still uplifting to the northeast and subduction was going on to the west. My resistant sandstones in western Grand Canyon have been stripped back to bare rock by erosion of the weak shales of the overlying Hermit Formation revealing the Esplanade Plateau.

285 Ma

Wescogame Formation of the Supai Group[42] records the demise of distant mountains.

Wecogame Formation, 300 million years old. This conglomerate sample has pebbles that were ripped up from its own sedimentary layers.

The Supai Group contains alternating layers of red sandstone, mudstone and limestone that give it a characteristic cliff-slope profile. The 18- foot-long raft (circled) looks tiny.

Supai Group

Esplanade Fm.

Wescogame Fm.

Manakacha Fm.

Watahomigi Fm.

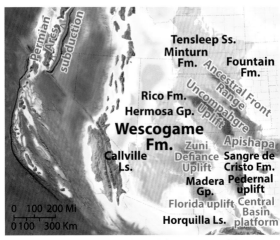

Permian Arc subduction

Tensleep Ss.
Minturn Fm.
Fountain Fm.
Ancestral Front Range
Rico Fm.
Hermosa Gp.
Uncompahgre Uplift
Wescogame Fm.
Zuni
Apishapa
Callville Ls.
Defiance Uplift
Sangre de Cristo Fm.
Madera Gp.
Pedernal uplift
Florida uplift
Central Basin platform
Horquilla Ls.

0 100 200 Mi
0 100   300 Km

Advance of the sea was winning the battle between sea and dunes.

My formal name is Wescogame Formation, the third layer from the bottom of the Supai Group. I was named for Wescagome Point, named for a family of the Havasupai people.

My rock type is a sedimentary rock, a conglomerate made up of clasts of other sedimentary rocks ripped up by the currents that deposited us. Most of my formation is made up of red sandstone. I am about the same age as the Callville Limestone that was being deposited in a shallow sea to the west.

My age is 295 million years on the Trail of Time, but 300 million years is my refined age. My fossils lived on Earth between 299 and 303 million years ago during the Pennsylvanian Period.

My story: I was deposited by rivers flowing through mud and sand flats. Conglomerates like me are seen near the upper part of the formation and help mark the boundary between the Pennsylvanian and Permian periods. The Ancestral Rocky Mountain were being uplifted and eroded to contribute to my sediments. Alternating sandstones and mudstones form many small cliffs and slopes.

295 Ma

Manakacha Formation of the Supai Group:[42] redbeds were deposited by continental-scale rivers.

Manakacha Formation, 315 million years old, see the burrows on the back side.

A trackway exposed in rockfall on the Bright Angel Trail. The identity of the animal is not known, but it was probably a very early reptile. The peculiar pattern of the footprints shows that the animal was either walking on a slope or was being pushed sideways by a strong wind (as depicted in the image). Artwork by Emily Waldman, courtesy of Steve Rowland, University of Nevada Las Vegas.

Continental-scale rivers brought some of my sediments from as far away as the Appalachian Mountains; other sediments came from the eroding Ancestral Rocky Mountains.

My formal name is Manakacha Formation of the Supai Group, second from the bottom and second oldest of my group. I get my name from Manakacha Point, named for a Havasupai family.

My rock type is a sedimentary rock. I am a reddish sandstone, the red color comes from iron oxide coatings that stain my sand grains like rust.

My age: I am at 305 million years old on the Trail of Time, but 315 million years is my refined age. My fossils lived on Earth between 314 and 317 million years ago during the Pennsylvanian Period.

My story: My layer was deposited as a series of quartz-rich sands and muds by rivers that flowed west towards the sea, and also by strong winds that eroded some of the riverbed sands and redeposited them as sand dunes. My sediment was derived from uplifting highlands of the Ancestral Rocky Mountains to the northeast that were eroding and causing rivers to get choked with sediment, and some of my zircon sand grains come from as far as away as the still-forming Appalachian Mountains.[45]

305 Ma

Watahomigi Formation of the Supai Group:[42] limestones were deposited when oceans prevailed.

Watahomigi Formation, 320 million years old.

My limestones are thin layers in eastern Grand Canyon but thicken to the west; they represent times when lime muds were being deposited in shallow oceans rather than coastal sand dunes.[42]

Eastward advance of the shoreline onto the land was due to rising sea levels.

My formal name is Watahomigi Formation of the Supai Group, the basal and oldest formation of the Supai Group. I am named for Watahomigi Point, named for a Havasupai family.

My rock type is a sedimentary rock. I am a limestone, from a gray limestone layer that is interbedded with red sandstone layers.

My age: I am located at 315 million years on the Trail of Time, but 320 million years is my refined central age. My fossils lived on Earth between 318 and 323 million years ago during the Pennsylvanian Period.

My story: I was deposited as a lime mud in a shallow sea. Water depth was fluctuating and shorelines were advancing farther onto the land as a result of rising sea levels. Sea level rise was caused by melting of the south pole glacial ice, similar to what is happening to Antarctica today. Dunes were around, but this was a time when the advance of the sea was winning the battle between sea and dunes. I got turned from lime mud into limestone as I got buried by younger layers.

Surprise Canyon Formation[43] was first formally described and dated in the 1980s.

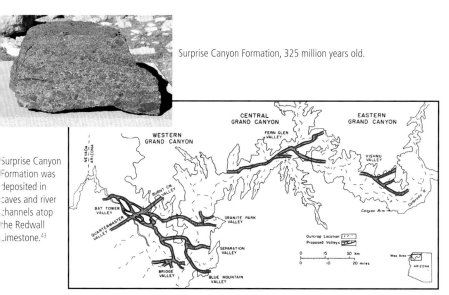

Surprise Canyon Formation, 325 million years old.

Surprise Canyon Formation was deposited in caves and river channels atop the Redwall Limestone.[43]

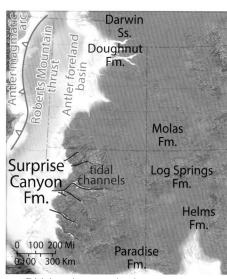

Tidal channels connected to the western seaway.

My formal name is Surprise Canyon Formation, named for Surprise Canyon in western Grand Canyon where I am well exposed.

My rock type is a sedimentary rock, specifically a conglomerate made up of pieces of underlying rock units, like limestone clasts from Redwall. Other rocks in my formation include sandstone, mudstone, and limestone.

My age is 320 million years on the Trail of Time, but 325 million years is my refined age. I have a very diverse assemblage of marine fossils that lived on Earth 324 to 326 million years ago during the Mississippian Period.

My story: I was deposited in a river system that flowed in valleys and filled collapsed caves on top of Redwall. Large estuaries led towards the shoreline located near present day Las Vegas. My discontinuous channels were not considered a separate layer until the middle 1970s and I was first named formally in 1985. Study of my fossils showed that I am several million years younger than Redwall (below me) and older than Supai (above me) so I'm glad to be my own separate formation.

320 Ma

Redwall Limestone[43] had diverse marine life — alike yet not alike to today's.

Redwall Limestone, 340 million years old. Oops, I should have been installed with my bedding horizontal.

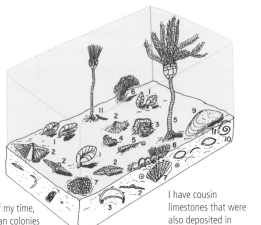

You should have seen the diverse marine life of my time, such as: brachiopods (1,2), crinoids (5), bryozoan colonies (6,8), corals (7), bivalves (9), gastopods (10), and others too.[43]

I have cousin limestones that were also deposited in Mississippian seas; fish had evolved and could swim from what is now Mexico to Canada.

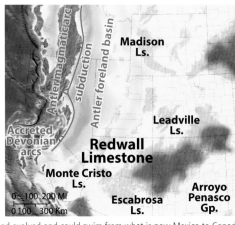

Antler magmatic arc · subduction · Antler foreland basin

Accreted Devonian arcs

Madison Ls.

Leadville Ls.

Redwall Limestone

Monte Cristo Ls.

Escabrosa Ls.

Arroyo Penasco Gp.

0 100 200 Mi
0 100 300 Km

My formal name is Redwall Limestone. I am representing all 4 of my members: Whitmore Wash, Thunder Springs, Mooney Falls, and Horseshoe Mesa. My name came from G.K. Gilbert (1875, who spelled me Red Wall) for my red appearance and the name was formalized by N. H. Darton (1910) who named Redwall Canyon.[33]

My rock type is a sedimentary rock. I am a gray limestone inside but my name reflects my skin-deep red coating that I get from iron oxide washing down from the Supai Group.

My age is 340 million years on the Trail of Time. My index fossils show that I was deposited deposited between 333 and 348 million years ago during the Mississippian Period.

My story: I was deposited as lime muds in a vast inland seaway that extended across most of the present western United States. Caves started developing even as I was becoming a rock; these got filled with overlying units like Surprise Canyon. Continued cave collapse and fluid movement formed ore deposits (breccia pipes) that have copper and uranium minerals in them (see page 127). Today I form nearly impassible and prominent cliffs that make it hard for animals and people to travel into and out of Grand Canyon. My caves and cracks also form a network for groundwater flow in the Redwall-Muav aquifer.

Temple Butte[44] identities: channel fill in the east; limestone in the west.

Temple Butte Formation, 380 million years old.

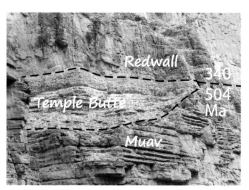

Eastern Grand Canyon tidal channels cut into the underlying Muav and show the location of a 164 million year time gap (a disconformity).

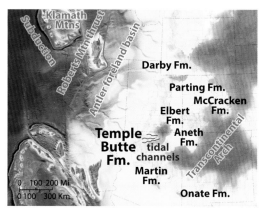

I was deposited as limestone in marine settings to the west and as sandstone and mudstone in rivers and tidal channels to the east.[44]

My formal name is Temple Butte Formation, named for a Butte in eastern Grand Canyon that does indeed look like a temple.

My rock type is a sedimentary rock. I am made up of limestone and dolostone (like limestone but with Mg as well as Ca in my carbonate) and my formation also includes sandstone and conglomerate.

My age: I am about 380 million years old. The fossils in my layers lived on Earth between 375 and 385 million years ago during the Devonian Period.

My story: I was deposited in channels within an intertidal zone with an open ocean to the west and restricted bays to the east. I can tell you about what was happening for part of the "time gap" between 504 and 340 million years ago. But in places where I was not deposited (or am not preserved) such as at the far right of the picture above, the disconformity contact between the Cambrian Muav (504 Ma) and Mississippian Redwall (340 Ma) represents about a 164 million year time gap. Things are clearer where I help mark the disconformity.

Muav Formation of the Tonto Group: a karst aquifer and a major host for groundwater.

Muav Limestone, 504 million years old. Feel the river polish and fluting on top, ouch!

Dutton Spring is a good example of how groundwater moves through cracks and caves and pours from solid rock to form springs, as demonstrated by Grand Canyon geologist Peter Huntoon.

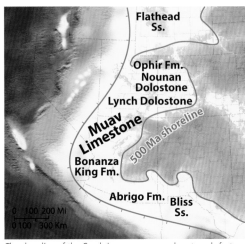

The shoreline of the Cambrian seaway moved eastwards fast between and 510 and 500 million years.

My formal name is Muav Limestone of the Tonto Group. I was named by John Wesley Powell in 1869 for Muav saddle; Muav is a Paiute word for "divide."

My rock type is a sedimentary rock. I am a limestone. My fossils include many species of trilobites and sponges and other marine invertebrates.

My age: I am 505 million years on the Trail of Time; my trilobite fossils lived on Earth 503 to 505 million years ago during the Cambrian Period.[30]

My story: I was deposited towards the end of the story of the rapid flooding of North America by a deepening ocean. I record the deeper water lime-mud deposited as the shoreline moved rapidly eastwards. Today, Redwall and I, although very different in age, have teamed up to be part of the most important regional aquifer (Redwall-Muav aquifer) that supplies groundwater for the Park. My interesting fluting was sculpted by the Colorado River as it carved Grand Canyon.

505 Ma

Bright Angel Shale of the Tonto Group: new trilobite species appeared and went extinct quickly.

Bright Angel Shale, 506 million years old. Trace the trilobite tracks (called *Cruziana*) and worm burrows on the top.

Cambrian time records an explosion in diversity of animal life on Earth. Tonto Group has 47 species of trilobites.

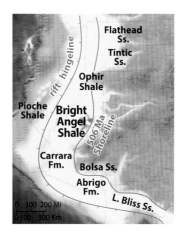

My sands and muds got covered by lime muds as the sea deepened.

My formal name is Bright Angel Shale of the Tonto Group. My rocks include sandstone, mudstone, and dolostone as well as shale. I get my name from Bright Angel Creek that was named by John Wesley Powell in 1869.

My rock type is a sedimentary rock. I am more sand-rich to the east where I am interlayered with Tapeats and more lime-rich to the west where I am interlayered with Muav.

My age is 515 million years on the Trail of Time but 506 million years is my refined age; my fossils lived on Earth from 505 to 507 million years ago during the Cambrian Period.[30]

My story: Our Tonto Group story is of the rapid flooding of North America during an eastward advance of the Cambrian seaway between 510 and 500 million years ago called the Sauk transgression. I'm the middle layer and was deposited as mud in off-shore but not deep-water environments. In outcrop, I am noted for my purple and green shales; the green color comes from the mineral glauconite that forms from the poop of animals. Mauv's lime muds were west of me and Tapeat's sands were east of me at any given time and the back and forth of the shoreline caused us to be interbedded at a given location. Now, my shale layers act as a barrier for groundwater that percolates downward through Muav such that there are many springs at our contact. I am soft and easy to erode and I form the Tonto Platform, a wide gentle area above Tapeat's cliffs in eastern Grand Canyon.

515 Ma

Tapeats Sandstone of the Tonto Group records rapid flooding of North America.

Look within the strata. Tapeats pinches out against paleo-islands made up of resistant Shinumo Sandstone that stuck up as the beach sands of the Tapeats Sandstone lapped around them.

Tapeats Sandstone, 508 million years old. Oops, I should have been installed with my bedding horizontal.

I have lots of cousin sheet sands of about the same age like Zabriskie in Nevada, Bolsa in Arizona, Bliss in New Mexico, Sawatch in Colorado, Flathead in Wyoming, and Potsdam in New York.

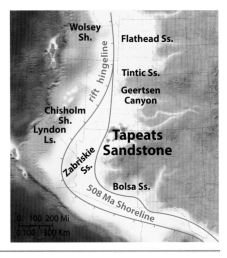

My formal name is Tapeats Sandstone of the Tonto Group. I was named for Tapeats Creek which was named by John Wesley Powell's second expedition (1872) after a Paiute named "Ta Pits" who claimed ownership.

My rock type is a sedimentary rock. I am made up almost entirely of sandstone. Touch my nice grainy sandstone with lots of interesting tracks and trails from burrowing worm-like animals, but few trilobite body fossils.

My age: I am at 525 million years on the Trail of Time, but 508 million years is my refined age.[30] In western Grand Canyon I am older than the 509 Ma Ollenellid trilobites. In eastern Grand Canyon I am younger than my youngest detrital sand grains that gave a U-Pb zircon age of 509 million years old.[30]

My story: I record a series of beach and near-shore sands that were deposited by tidal currents as the Cambrian seaway flooded across North America. I filled local depressions on the long-weathered Great Unconformity surface that had beveled into underlying Precambrian rocks. There were islands, especially of Shinumo Sandstone, sticking up that I could not cover, but the Bright Angel did. Where I was deposited on the 1.84 billion-year-old Elves Chasm gneiss, there are 1.3 billion years of time missing, but only 200 million years missing where I rest on the Chuar Group.

525
Ma

Sixtymile Formation: Tonto Group's newest family member.

Grand Canyon Supergroup: Sixtymile Formation, 510 million years old. I am now known to be Cambrian in age[30] and a new addition to the Tonto Group.

I was folded just before Tapeats was deposited flat on top of me.

Tapeats

Upper Sixtymile

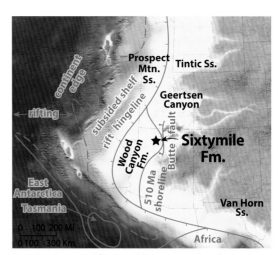

I record early stages of flooding of the sea across the subsiding continental shelf 510-500 million years ago. The Cambrian oceans advanced more recently and more rapidly than previously thought.

My formal name is Sixtymile Formation. I was named for Sixtymile Canyon which is 60 river miles below Lees Ferry. My family association is changing — I will soon formally be the Sixtymile Formation of the Tonto Group.

My rock type is a sedimentary rock, specifically a conglomerate. I am called a breccia in samples like this one with angular clasts.

My age: I was thought to be about 650 million years old when the Trail of Time was installed but 510 million years is a better estimate for my upper layers because new U-Pb radiometric dating of some of my zircon sand grains gives 509 million years old. Yikes, I am no longer in the Precambrian Grand Canyon Supergroup and instead am part of the Cambrian Tonto Group.

My story: I am joining the Tonto Group in telling the earliest part of the Cambrian story. I have large landslide blocks and soft sediment folds and slumps that reflect fault movement on the Butte fault that took place when the continent was being rifted. My lower layers are younger than the 527 Ma grains within them; my upper layers, labeled above, are younger than 509 Ma.

650 Ma

Walcott Member of the Kwagunt Formation of the Chuar Group had "vampires" and victims.

Walcott member, 729 million years old at its top.

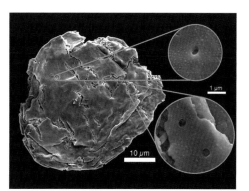

These are tiny flattened organic remains of single-celled microfossils showing evidence of tiny 'drill holes' made by single-celled "vampire-like" predators that sucked out and ate the organic matter;[46] photo courtesy of Susannah Porter.

Two dolostone layers within black shales of the Walcott Member on Nankoweap Butte are called the Couplet. The upper white line shows a 200 million year time gap (unconformity) between the Walcott Member and the Sixtymile Formation.

My name is the Walcott Member. I am the top member of the Kwagunt Formation of the Chuar Group of the Grand Canyon Supergroup. I was named for a place in the Chuar Valley that was named for geologist Charles Doolittle Walcott who worked in Grand Canyon in the 1880s and who discovered sub-mm-sized single-celled organisms that he named *Chuaria*.

My rock type is a sedimentary rock, specifically a shale. I am very black because I have up to 10% organic carbon in me. My member also has dolostone beds such as the the Flakey Dolostone near the base and the Couplet in the middle.

My age is 742 million on the Trail of Time, but 729 million years is my new age. Zircon grains in a 1-cm-thick ash bed at the top of my layer have been re-dated as 729 ± 1 million years old using the U-Pb radiometric dating method.[47] All my layers were deposited between about 740 and 729 million years ago.

My story: I was deposited in a shallow seaway that extended from here to Death Valley to northern Utah. I had an important influence leading into the Snowball Earth time of global glaciations that came after me, at 717 million years ago. I contain abundant micro-fossils. Life, oceans, and atmosphere were having trouble equilibrating with each other such that when abundant single-celled organisms sank to the seafloor they carried their carbon with them, lowering atmospheric CO_2 which made climate cooler.

742 Ma

Awatubi Member of the Chuar Group had vase-shaped "vampires," the first heterotrophs.

Awatubi Member, 750 million years old.

The brain bed is a stromatolite formed by single-celled algae in algal colonies.

Shales in the Chuar Group contain vase-shaped microfossils (at right) of shell-forming amoebae. The semi-circular holes in the lower right one formed when single-celled predators attacked the amoeba's shell. Each shell is about 1/10 of a millimeter long; these tiny fossils are called microfossils.[46] Photo courtesy of Susannah Porter.

My formal name is the Awatubi Member. I am the middle member of the Kwagunt Formation of the Chuar Group of the Grand Canyon Supergroup. I was named for Awatubi Canyon, itself named after the Hopi village of Awatovi, a now-abandoned Hopi pueblo that was visited by García López de Cárdenas in 1540 and where a mission was built by Friar Francisco de Porras in 1629.

My rock type is a sedimentary rock. I am a stromatolitic dolostone whereas most of my member is black shale. Geologic mappers nick-named me the "brain bed"; you can see why. Check out my seating rock samples near Headquarters portal.

My age is 751 ± 8 million years old near my base as shown by a Re-Os radiometric age on marcasite nodules a bit above the brain bed.[47] Thus, my layer plus Walcott were deposited between about 751 and 729 million years ago.

My story: The shallow Chuar seaway I was deposited in, and changing climate conditions, were exciting times for single-celled life. My shales contain vase-shaped microfossils which were the first heterotrophic organisms on Earth, tiny single-celled organisms that, like "vampires," ate other organisms rather than getting all their energy from the sun. Now, my dolostones form ledges and cliffs but my shales are easily weathered and form slopes.

Carbon Butte Member of the Kwagunt Formation of the Chuar Group was deposited in tidal conditions.

Carbon Butte Member, 753 million years old.

This is a tilted bedding plane that was originally horizontal and is now sloping towards us in the Chuar syncline.

The U-shaped fold (Chuar syncline) was forming as I was being deposited and records Chuar basin subsidence due to movement on the Butte fault.[48]

My formal name is Carbon Butte Member; I am the lowest member of the Kwagunt Formation of the Chuar Group of the Grand Canyon Supergroup. My name comes from Carbon Butte in eastern Grand Canyon, named by Charles Dolittle Walcott in the 1880s. This comes from chief Chuarrumpeak of the Kaibab Paiute tribe who was introduced to John Wesley Powell by Jacob Hamblin.

My rock type is a sedimentary rock, a red sandstone at my base and white sandstone at my top.

My age: I am at 760 million years on the Trail of Time but my refined age is between 751 and 757 million years old; older than the 751 million-year-old Awatubi just above me and younger than the 757 million-year-old Carbon Canyon Member, two layers below me.

My story: I was deposited in a tidal environment near the shoreline of the shallow Chuar seaway. I was cemented by silica and form a resistant cliff in the Chuar Valley.

760 Ma

Duppa Member of the Galeros Formation of the Chuar Group: stacks of mudstone.

Duppa Member, 755 million years old.

My shales are easily weathered and form slopes. Like all of the Chuar Group, I am only exposed in Chuar Valley of eastern Grand Canyon, a stark and beautiful landscape that few get to see.

Carbon Butte
Duppa
Carbon Canyon

The **ChUMP** seaway extended from (and was named for) outcrops of the **Ch**uar, **U**inta **M**ountain, and **P**ahrump[17] groups that were deposited at about the same time.

rifting of Rodinia
rift margin
Chump seaway
Cordilleran rift hingeline
Uinta Mtn. Gp. 800 Ma
edge of North American basement
East Antarctica
Upper Pahrump Gp. 775 Ma
Chuar Group
Togari Gp.
Caborca
Tasmania
Las Viboras
Africa

0 100 200 Mi
0 100   300 Km

EXPLANATION
0.8 Ga STRUCTURES AND SEDIMENTS
AREA OF INFERRED CHUMP SEAWAY
RAPID COOLING AT 800 Ma

My formal name is Duppa Member, youngest of the Galeros Formation of the Chuar Group of the Grand Canyon Supergroup. My name comes from Duppa Butte, that was named for "Lord" Darrell Duppa who was born in France, served in the English army, came to Arizona in 1863, and named Phoenix and Tempe..

My rock type is a sedimentary rock; I have layers of red sandstone and mudstone.

My age: I am older than Carbon Butte above me, but have the same age brackets, younger than the 757 million-year-old Carbon Canyon Member below us and older than the 751 million-year-old Awatubi Member above us.

My story: I am not the flashiest part of the Chuar Group; I do not have dolostone marker layers and I am gradational with the layer below me. The 757 and 751 million year dates from layers below and above me indicate that my 200 m of mudstone in between these dated layers were deposited in about 6 million years at an average sedimentation rate of 33 m/Ma. The Chuar basin was subsiding by rifting on the Butte fault to allow sediment to accumulate.

770 Ma

Carbon Canyon Member of the Galeros Formation of the Chuar Group: seas dried out and polygonal cracks formed.

Carbon Canyon Member, 757 million years old. Deep mud cracks reflect times when the basin dried out.

Step around to see my back side where a white lime-mud filled a deep crack within gray/tan layered carbonate mud.

In Chuar Valley, mountains of shale of Chuar Group form a spectacular "moonscape" that few get to see. There is a person inside the circle that gives a sense of the scale.

My formal name is Carbon Canyon Member of the Galeros Formation of the Chuar Group of the Grand Canyon Supergroup.
My rock type is a sedimentary rock; I am dolostone and I alternate in a cyclic way with shales and sandstones. One marker bed in my layer, besides myself, is a type of fossilized algal colony (stromatolite) called *Baicallia* that looks like a batch of cauliflowers.
My age: I am 757 ± 7 million years old based on a Re-Os radiometric age on my organic-rich shales.[47]
My story: My layers tell a story of rhythmically alternating cycles of deeper and shallower water. I am a good example of when the basin dried out and mudcracks formed in the carbonate. These are polygonal on bedding surfaces and look like dagger-shaped cracks filled with light colored lime mud, that protrude down into the gray dolostone. Mappers call me the polygonal bed and I can be traced across many areas of the Chuar Valley.

780 Ma

Jupiter Member of the Galeros Formation of the Chuar Group: single celled algae ruled.

Inzeria stromatolite of the Jupiter Member, 765 million years old.

The 2009 samples of Jupiter fractured and were never mounted. In the meantime, visitors often put a piece of Kaibab on the empty plinth or found other uses for it.

Tanner Shales

Inzeria

Geologists examine *Inzeria* bed with red and green shales of the Jupiter Member above.

My formal name is Jupiter Member of the Galeros Formation of the Chuar Group of the Grand Canyon Supergroup. My name is from Jupiter Temple above Chuar Creek.

My rock type is a sedimentary rock. I am stromatolitic dolostone (similar to a limestone but with more of the element Mg). I am a marker layer at the base of the member and much of my layer above me is made up of black, red, and green shale.

My age: I was placed at 790 million years on the Trail of Time but 765 million years is my refined age; newer dates indicate I was deposited sometime between 775 and 757 million years ago based on my position as older than (below) Carbon Canyon and younger than (above) the Nankoweap Formation.

My story: Stromatolites in the Chuar Group, like me, reflect mound-shaped algal colonies that grew in a shallow sea; but each of us is different. I am called *Inzeria* whereas Carbon Canyon's are called *Baicalia* and Awatubi's are called *Boxonia*. We look different, not necessarily because the single-celled algae were different, but because the conditions for the algae growth had different water depths, currents, and sediment inputs. I was re-collected in 2016 because the 2009 sample broke and was never installed on my plinth. Some visitors called Park Rangers to report: "someone stole Jupiter." Rangers set a piece of local rock (Kaibab) as a stand-in to cut down the phone calls.

Tanner Member of the Galeros Formation of the Chuar Group: limestones recrystallized to dolostone.

Tanner Member, 770 million years old.

Tanner Shales

Tanner Dolostone

Tanner dolostone and shale occur in a fault block along the Nankoweap Trail in Nankoweap Canyon.

My formal name is the Tanner Member of the Galeros Formation of the Chuar Group of the Grand Canyon Supergroup. I got my name from Tanner Canyon that was named for Seth Tanner who in 1889 helped develop a trail to the Colorado River now called the Tanner Trail.

My rock type is a sedimentary rock. I am a dolostone (similar to a limestone, but with Mg as well as Ca in my carbonate). Much of the member above me is made up of black shale containing the single celled fossil *Chuaria*.

My age: I was placed at 800 million years on the Trail of Time but 770 million years is my refined age. I was deposited sometime between 775 and 757 million years ago based on my position below the dated rocks of Carbon Canyon and above Nankoweap.

My story: My member started out as a chemical sediment in the shallow Chuar seaway then more muds were brought in. I got recrystallized in place which is why my crystals are coarse grained.

800 Ma

Chuar Group's newest family member: Nankoweap is younger than we thought.

Nankoweap Formation, 775 million years old.

Nankoweap Formation has a lower red sandstone and an upper white sandstone, both beneath the Tanner dolostone.

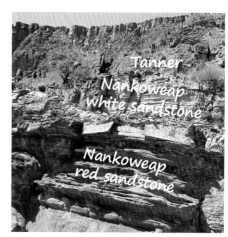

My formal name is the Nankoweap Formation of the Grand Canyon Supergroup; I am now joining the Chuar Group although I used to be considered a different unit.

My rock type is a sedimentary rock. I am red sandstone; touch and polish my ripple marks please! These formed as currents washed back and forth in a shallow Chuar seaway, but nearer the shore than most layers of the overlying shale layers.

My age: I am less than 780 million years old. I was placed at 900 million on the Trail of Time because my iron minerals were aligned as if I was deposited in North America at that time (from paleomagnetism studies), but newer dates on my zircon sand grains show I am younger than the 780 million-year-old zircon grains within me.[17]

My story: What a change in my self image! I always felt close to Tanner dolostone and now I find out we are about the same age. These 780-million-year-old grains were dated by the U-Pb radiometric method. Obviously, the grains had to exist before they were washed into my layer so I know I was deposited after 780 Ma but before the 757 Ma Carbon Canyon way above me. I sit above the Cardenas Basalt with an angular unconformity indicating underlying layers were faulted and tilted before my time.

900 Ma

Cardenas Basalt: 1.1 billion year old lava flows filled faulted valleys.

Cardenas Basalt, 1,104 million years old. This 2010 sample cracked.

In 2016, a Cardenas replacement sample was collected.

1.1 billion year old lava flows and the Butte fault.

My formal name is Cardenas Basalt of the Unkar Group of the Grand Canyon Supergroup. My name comes from Cardenas Butte and Cardenas Creek, both named for Garcia Lopez de Cárdenas, the Spanish explorer who, in 1540, was the first European to see Grand Canyon.

My rock type is an igneous rock; I am a basalt, crystallized from a lava flow.

My age: I crystallized about 1,104 million years ago based on Ar-Ar dating.[48]

My story: I am from a thick sequence of lava flows that reach a thickness of 300 m (see above). The vent areas where I flowed from are unknown. I am the same age and composition (but different texture) as the diabase sills and dikes that intruded the Unkar Group and that carried magma upwards. My lava flows filled valleys formed from NE-SW extension of the region. After I crystallized, there were copper-bearing fluids that filled my cracks and gas bubbles with blue copper oxide mineral (can you see them?). I am only exposed in eastern Grand Canyon where I form striking black cliffs.

1,130 Ma

Dox Formation of the Unkar Group: redbeds with filled mud cracks.

Dox Formation, 1,120 million years old. Trace my casts of mudcracks that formed on the bottom of a bed.

Dox Formation is the thickest sedimentary unit in Grand Canyon — up to 1,000 meters thick

of redbeds! They were deposited from N-flowing rivers coming from a continent-continent collisional mountain belt in the Texas region shown in the map.[48] The NW compression of the continent caused NE extension and resulted in faulting and tilting of the Unkar Group.

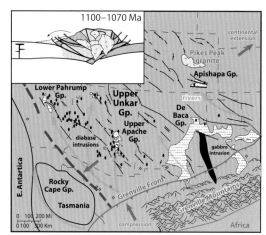

My formal name is the Dox Formation of the Unkar Group of the Grand Canyon Supergroup. I was named for Dox Castle which was named for Miss Virginia Dox who visited Grand Canyon in the 1800s. I am representing my four members: Escalante Creek, Soloman Temple, Comanche Pont, and Ochoa Point.

My rock type is a sedimentary rock. I am a red sandstone.

My age: I was deposited in the time period between 1,130 and 1,100 million years ago; I am older than the 1,104 million-year-old Cardenas Basalt layer above me and I was deposited after my youngest zircon sand grains dated so far that give a U-Pb zircon radiometric age of 1,130 million years old.[49]

My story: I was deposited by rivers that flowed all the way from the area that is now Texas, where the Himalayan-scale Grenville Mountains were steadily eroding. You can see ripple marks and mud cracks and even billion-year-old raindrop impressions in my sandstones. I am underappreciated; my layers are about 1,000-meters thick, more than any other formation in the Grand Canyon region. But they are tilted so that my great thickness is hard to appreciate until you go to Lipan Point or Hopi Watchtower for an eyeful of my redbeds! (see page 41).

Shinumo Sandstone of the Unkar Group: first I rippled, then I cracked.

Shinumo Sandstone is about 1,130 million years old. Note the ripple marks and the mud cracks on the top bedding surface.

Shinumo

diabase dike

Hakatai

Shinumo Sandstone forms steep cliffs above Hakatai Shale. The Hance diabase dike, depicted here cross cutting Hakatai, turns parallel to bedding and becomes a sill near the base of the Shinumo Sandstone.

Convolute deformation features record earthquakes and dewatering that took place when the sediments were soft, over 1 billion years ago.

My formal name is Shinumo Sandstone[16] of the Unkar Group of the Grand Canyon Supergroup. I was named for Shinumo Altar and Shinumo Canyon. These places were named by Frederick Dellenbaugh in about 1872; he got the name from the Paiute word for "old people, cliff dwellers."

My rock type is a sedimentary rock. I have been called quartzite as I am almost entirely (> 95%) quartz grains, but this term is better used for metamorphosed sandstone, which I am not. But I AM strongly silica cemented and as hard as many metamorphic quartzites.

My age: I am 1,140 to 1,100 million years old, beneath Dox and Cardenas, so older than them. I was placed at 1,170 on the Trail of Time, but my youngest zircon sand grains have been dated as 1,150 million years old by the U-Pb radiometric method.[49]

My story: I was deposited by far-traveled rivers, like Dox, but reworked by tidal currents that flowed back and forth as shown by my symmetrical ripple marks. The mudcracked ripples show times of drying out. When I was still soft sediment, there were large earthquakes that formed my convolute bedding, called seismites. I was cemented into a very resistant rock, probably during Cardenas time, was tilted in fault blocks, and have always formed strong cliffs. For example, my cliffs were exposed as islands (monadnocks) in the Cambrian seaway 500 million years ago that were only gradually covered by the Tonto Group.

Hakatai Shale of the Unkar Group: rippled sandstone and colorful slopes.

Hakatai Shale, 1,230 million years old.

This view on the Bright Angel Trail shows my tilted redbeds. Across the Colorado River is the Great Unconformity, with Tapeats on top of Vishnu Schist, but with no Hakatai present over there.

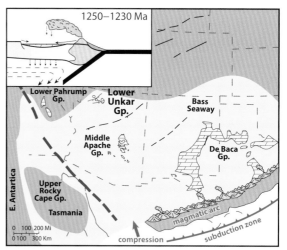

Bass and Hakatai were deposited in a seaway north of a developing magmatic arc and subduction zone system located in what is now the Texas area. Adjacent continents to the west included parts of Antarctica and Australia.

My formal name is Hakatai Shale of the Unkar Group of the Grand Canyon Supergroup.

My rock type is a sedimentary rock. I am a red sandstone like many layers in the Hakatai; my formation is called shale, but both sandstone and mudstone are present.

My age: 1,255 to 1,230 million years are the ages of my youngest detrital zircon grains dated so far with the U-Pb radiometric method.[49]

My story: I have a gradational contact with the underlying Bass Formation and there is a disconformity (time missing) at my upper contact with Shinumo. The ripple marks that you see are getting nicely polished (please help). They are symmetrical ripples from wave currents oscillating back and forth. Some think me to be bragging but it is true when I say I am the most colorful formation in Grand Canyon —bright orange. I form slopes that can be seen from Yavapai Geology Museum and from many places along the Trail of Time.

1,180 Ma

Bass Formation of the Unkar Group: old life and young metamorphism in Grand Canyon.

Bass Formation, 1,255 million years old. These two rocks look very different but both are from the Bass Formation. The white one was metamorphosed into a marble by an intruding 1.1 billion-year-old diabase sill. The red one contains stromatolites.

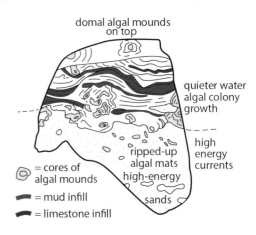

domal algal mounds on top

quieter water algal colony growth

high energy currents

ripped-up algal mats high-energy

high-energy

sands

= cores of algal mounds

= mud infill

= limestone infill

The oldest fossilized life in Grand Canyon's rocks is in the form of stromatolites. These domes are algal colonies that grew in shallow oceans and were later turned to limestone. Wave energy ripped apart some of the colonies.

My formal name is Bass Formation of the Unkar Group of the Grand Canyon Supergroup. I am named for Bass Canyon, named for William Wallace Bass who, with wife Ada Lenore, raised a family on the south rim in the early 1900s.

My rock type is a sedimentary rock. I am a limestone and I am interlayered with sandstones and conglomerates. I was metamorphosed from a limestone to this white marble in places where I was heated by intrusion of diabase sills 1.1 billion years ago.

My age: 1,255 ± 2 million years old is the age of a volcanic ash that fell into the Bass seaway and became a layer within limestones.[16] Its zircon grains were dated by U-Pb radiometric dating. I was located at 1,190 million years on the Trail of Time so I'd like to be moved to the correct location at some point.

My story: I was deposited in a shallow seaway that had algal stromatolites in it. These are structures built by single celled algae and are the oldest life recorded in Grand Canyon rocks. A representative of these stromatolites can be seen at marker 1,160 on the Trail of Time, and in the picture and sketch shown above. The stromatolites dome upwards showing how algal colonies grew in the shallow seaway to get closer to their source of energy, the sun; then waves and currents ripped and shredded the algal mats. I was deposited in fault blocks as North America was being squeezed NW-SE and stretched NE-SW; this is what caused tilting of the Unkar Group.

1,190 Ma

Hotauta Member of the Bass Formation has a basal conglomerate with a well-rounded family of immigrants.

Houtauta Member, 1,255 million years old. Conglomerate was deposited above the Great Unconformity. It is called a nonconformity here because sedimentary rocks (above) rest on igneous and metamorphic rocks (below). The rocks below were metamorphosed at 20 km depths at 1.7 billion years ago[50] and unroofed by Bass time at 1.25 billion years ago following the erosional demise of the Vishnu Mountains.

My formal name is Hotauta Member of the Bass Formation of the Unkar Group of the Grand Canyon Supergroup. I was named for Hotauta amphitheater, itself named for Hotouta, a great Havasupai leader.

My rock type is a sedimentary rock. I am a conglomerate and I am interlayered with sandstone and limestones.

My age: I am immediately below the Bass ash layer and hence very close in age to its 1,255-million-year-old U-Pb zircon age.

My story: You can see the coarse pebbles of granite and schist and pegmatite that were eroded from steep-sided islands that protruded from the shallow seaway 1.25 billion years ago. Look for rocks like these cobbles farther west along the Trail of Time. The gray quartzites are not known from the local basement but are similar to quartzites known from areas to the south, near present-day Prescott and Payson.[51] The rest of these well-rounded "immigrant" cobbles came from nearby eroding basement granites and schists. My member records high energy streams bringing cobbles into the sea. Interlayered conglomerate and limestone is an odd combination—indicating fault movement along the sides of the islands where rivers dumped into a shallow seaway.

Stories From Grand Canyon's Rocks

1,200 Ma

Quartermaster granite, I'm a loner on the Trail of Time.

Quartermaster granite, 1,375 million years old.

Before the rock was installed, visitors thought up other uses for the plinth.

Quartermaster granite crops out beneath the Great Unconformity which is a nonconformity in western Grand Canyon.

My formal name is Quartermaster granite; I was named for Quartermaster Canyon which was named for a Hualapai quartermaster who lived there in the early 1900s.

My rock type is an igneous rock, a granite. My pink mineral is potassium feldspar, the white is plagioclase feldspar, my gray/clear mineral is quartz. See if you can see all three minerals.

My age is 1,375 ± 2 million years old. I am the only known representative in Grand Canyon of a widespread group of granites that intruded in central Arizona and all across the southwestern U.S. about 1.4 billion years ago.[52]

My story: I was formed by melting of the lower crust, then my magma rose buoyantly to the middle crust and crystallized at about 10-km depths. Erosion between 1,375 and 1,250 million years ago wore away the crust above me to bring me to Earth's surface by about 1,255 million years ago. In the past 6 million years, the Colorado River cut through to where I was sampled in western Grand Canyon, just below the Great Unconformity.

1,375 Ma

Phantom granite: hot and cold; first I crystallized from a magma, recently I was smoothed by the river.

Phantom granite, 1,662 million years old.

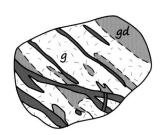

Sketch it to see it: this granite has different "flavors" (like swirled ice cream); darker patches were mingling with the lighter patches when the magma crystallized; then last fluids filled cracks (the red dikes).

Phantoms here? Phantom granite is exposed in the walls of Phantom Creek, shown here. The creek is flowing left (W) to right (E) to join Bright Angel Creek just above Phantom Ranch, then to the Colorado River to the right of this photo.

My formal name is Phantom granite. I was named for Phantom Canyon, a narrow slot canyon in the bottom of Grand Canyon. It was named by the USGS in 1906 because of tales about it being haunted. Mary Colter, architect, gave the same name to Phantom Ranch in the 1920s.

My rock type is granite; the dark parts are granite, just a bit older than the light colored veins, that are also granite.

My age is 1,662 ± 1 million years old.[53] I am one of the youngest granites, except for the Quartermaster granite.

My story: I was intruded as a magma after the arc collisions of the Yavapai orogeny had ended but the lower crust was still hot and melts continued to move upwards. I was not deformed and hence have little in the way of deformational layering (foliation). Not many people get to see my cliffs because they are hidden away in steep-walled Phantom Canyon. The stories about the phantoms in my canyon are exaggerated. I have only seen a few and I have been in there for the entire 2 million years it has taken Phantom Creek to carve this gorge. Once I became exposed by erosion in Phantom Canyon, my rock had wild rides in several flash floods, first into Bright Angel Creek, then into the Colorado River. I was collected in the river near the mouth of Bright Angel Creek, where I acquired my polish. My story involved both great heat and the cold river. I wouldn't change a minute of it.

1,662 Ma

Cremation pegmatite: last melts to crystallize.

Cremation pegmatite, 1,698 million years old.

Think of the muscovite and quartz in this pocket between the feldspars as the very last of the fluids to crystallize from a granitic melt.

Pegmatite swarms near Crystal Creek represent last melts of granitic magma systems that were migrating upwards from the lower crust and got frozen here, which was in the middle crust at that time, about 1.7 billion years ago.

My formal name: I was named for Cremation Creek that enters the Colorado River just above Phantom Ranch; the name came from Cremation Point.

My rock type is pegmatite. I am similar to most granites in composition but I have much bigger crystals; you can see large micas in pods between my large crystals.

My age is 1,698 ± 1 million years; but other pegmatite swarms probably span between 1,700 and 1,680 million years old.[54]

My story: I represent four main swarms of pegmatite dikes that intruded Grand Canyon's older basement rocks in the Lower, Middle, and Upper Granite Gorges. Partial melting of the deeper crust caused my parent magmas to ascend to about 10-km depths where they squeezed into the layered rocks like an ice cream cone pushed into the pages of a book. The Yavapai orogeny arc collision was ending but not quite over, so some of my dikes were folded. Today, I think I give basement rocks their sense of color and complexity (and gnarlyness).

1,698 Ma

Horn Creek pluton was hot, twice.

Horn Creek pluton, 1,713 million years old, with pegmatite pods, veins, and dikes.

Sketch it to see it: the main rock is a foliated granodiorite in which melt pods of pegmatitic granite formed and were stretched during peak metamorphism.

Horn Creek pluton, the blotches show that I got hot a second time — hot enough to partially re-melt.

My formal name: I was named for Horn Creek that, in 1906, was named for Tom Horn, army scout, adventurer, deputy, rancher, Rough Rider, cattle detective, and finally convicted murderer.

My rock type is igneous, a granodiorite. I am similar to granite but darker. The pink pods and veins are melt pods and veins of granite and pegmatite.

My age is 1,713 ± 2 million years old.[53]

My story: I am the youngest from my group of granodiorites that were derived above a subduction zone as the Yavapai and Matatzal volcanic island chains collided (see page 96). Faint darkish blobs in the gray areas show mingling of different magmas (gabbro and granodiorite) as I was first crystallizing to become a rock. The light isolated pods are granite pegmatites that formed later, during metamorphism about 1.7 billion years ago. That reheating was at about 600 degrees Celsius, not as hot as my melts had been originally (closer to 800 Celsius), but hot enough that I partially melted again (for me it was like sweating on a hot day). These melt pods migrated and joined to form the pegmatite veins and these got pulled apart like taffy as shown by the arrows in the sketch above.

1,713 Ma

Ruby pluton: resistant to change.

Ruby pluton is 1,716 million years old. I am a metagabbro; if you look closely with the magnifer on your phone you can see that my white minerals are plagioclase feldspar, still in prismatic crystals just as they crystallized; my dark matrix is mainly hornblende.

During plate collisions I tended to crack into interesting crack networks (rather than flow), and pegmatite melts filled those cracks about 1.7 billion years ago.

My formal name is Ruby pluton, named for Ruby Canyon and the rapid it makes on the Colorado River.

My rock type is an igneous rock. I am a metagabbro and part of a granodiorite/diorite/gabbro pluton that formed above a subduction zone. These rock names refer to different rock compositions. Different quartz content, types of feldspar, and Fe and Mg content produce melts and resulting rocks that are different shades of gray. I am proud to be one of the darkest (most mafic).

My age is $1,716 \pm 0.5$ million years old;[53] wow that is a precise age!

My story: A pluton is a name for a batch of melt that gets intruded into the crust; these intrusions are bigger than a dike and smaller than a batholith. I am the largest pluton exposed in Grand Canyon and nearly a batholith in size if you consider how far I extend to the north and south of the granite gorges under the flat lying strata. My parent melts came from the mantle and helped build a large magmatic arc complex. Even when I was solidified and buried to great depths, my feldspar-rich composition made me difficult to deform so I generally don't have a strong deformational layering even though I've seen as much deformation as the rest of the basement rocks. During metamorphism some of my dark (mafic) grains changed from pyroxene to amphibole, but all in all I am pretty resistant to change and you can still see my original feldspar crystal shapes.

1,716 Ma

Deformed rocks are happy rocks.

Vishnu Schist, granodiorite, and folded pegmatite, all together.

Ask this "Rosetta Stone" Trail of Time rock about its sequence of events #1–5; then ask it how much it was squeezed during plate collisions (#5).

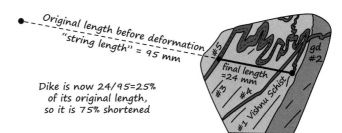

Dike is now 24/95=25% of its original length, so it is 75% shortened

STRAIN is the change in shape of a rock and can be measured by seeing how the distance between points changed from before to after the rock deformation. Final length divided by initial length = 24/95 = 25%, so I have been shortened by about 75%.

My formal name is Vishnu Schist; I am a nice example — sort of a Rosetta Stone — to help decode processes that operate in the deep crust during plate collisions.

My rock type includes schist, granodiorite, and pegmatite, a microcosm of the Vishnu basement rocks of the Granite Gorges.

My age spans much of the Yavapai orogeny, from my 1.75 billion year old schist,[54] to the 1.74–1.71 billion-year-old granodiorites (I am similar to Zoroaster and Horn Creek), to the 1.70 billion-year-old pegmatite (similar to Cremation).

My story: Follow the numbers in the sketch above to hear my story. #1) I was originally a sedimentary rock (graywacke) deposited by undersea turbidity flows in the sea. During the plate collisions I was buried to 20-km depths by thrust slices of other rocks and became metamorphosed into a schist. While down there, a gray igneous rock (#2) intruded as melt and crystallized as granodiorite. #3) Both my schist and granodiorite were squeezed at high temperature in the Earth and flowed like taffy so that minerals rotated perpendicular to the squeezing direction to form my metamorphic layering; the lines show the resulting foliation. #4) A thin granite melt intruded into a semi-straight crack and crystallized as a pegmatite dike. #5) This was cross cut by dike # 5; it started out straight too, then was dramatically folded. This folding provides a way to measure the amount the crust was shortened in the later stages of plate collision.

1,720 Ma

Trinity pluton formed in an oceanic island arc.

Trinity pluton, 1,730 million years ago.

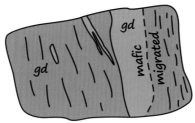

Sketch it to see it: Trinity pluton has mafic dikes (purple) that intruded and mingled with the granodiorite magma as it crystallized. It is strongly foliated (shown by the lines) and has a gneissic texture.

Growth of continental crust takes place by collision of volcanic island chains, called arcs, across subduction zones. Currently exposed basement rocks were down 20 km, at the level of the red arrows. Brown blobs below the level of the red arrows depict the Diamond Creek, Ruby, Trinity, Horn Creek, and Zoroaster plutons.

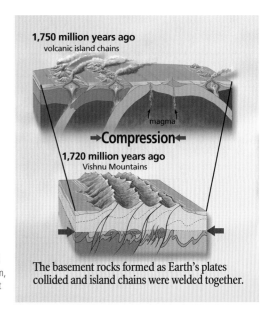

The basement rocks formed as Earth's plates collided and island chains were welded together.

My formal name is Trinity pluton, collected in the mouth of Trinity Canyon.

My rock type is an igneous rock, a granodiorite. My black stripe of gabbro was a dike of mafic melt from the mantle that was recharging the magma chamber.

My age is 1,730 ± 93 million years old. This is fairly imprecise but similar in age to the other granodiorites.

My story: There are several of us of similar age and composition that indicate we were all part of a subduction-related magmatic arc system. Like Zoroaster, I have a strong tectonic layering (foliation) that formed during deformation as plates collided. The location of the suture was Crystal shear zone a few river miles downstream.[55]

1,730 Ma

Diamond Creek pluton: a blended family.

Diamond Creek pluton, 1,736 million years old.

Sketch it to see the details of a frozen-in magma mingling factory. The darkest and highest temperature is gabbro (gb = purple), intermediate is diorite (d), lightest is granodiorite (gd = gray) which was the last melt to crystallize at about 700 degrees Celcius.

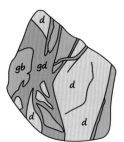

Dark gabbro melts were mostly solidified when they cracked and were pulled apart by invading lighter-colored (lower temperature) granodiorite melt.

F.W. Egloffsteiin's "Big Cañon at the Mouth of Diamond River" painting from the Ives expedition depicts (with only some exaggeration) vertical canyon walls near the mouth of Diamond Creek.

My formal name is Diamond Creek pluton, named from Diamond Canyon in western Grand Canyon that was named in 1858 by Lt. Joseph Christmas Ives and Dr. John S. Newberry. Ives expedition artwork shows vertical cliff walls where Diamond Creek cuts through my rocks.

My rock type is an igneous rock, mostly diorite. Overall, my pluton is mostly granodiorite (higher silica). My magma chamber was a mixing and mingling factory of different melt compositions that range from dark gabbro to gray granite. The gabbro came from the mantle and differentiated into the gray stuff.

My age is 1,736 ± 1 million years old.[53]

My story: Like my other cousin plutons, I crystallized from gabbro-diorite-granodiorite magmas that were mingling and mixing. When magmas mingle, they are like oil and water and can't mix completely. When magmas mix, it is more like coffee and cream — you get a result whose color depends on how much of each is in the mix. See if you can spot parts of my rock from all three parent magmas.

Stories From Grand Canyon's Rocks

1,736
Ma

Zoroaster pluton: hot stuff.

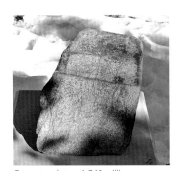

Zoroaster pluton, 1,740 million years old.

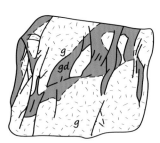

Sketch it to see the more felsic (g = granite) and intermediate (gray = gd = granodiorite) patches that represent magmas that were mingling when I crystallized; the dark cracks are lined by magmatic biotites.

Zoroaster pluton forms impressive cliffs in the Upper Granite Gorge of Grand Canyon, just beneath Yavapai Geology Museum.

My formal name is Zoroaster pluton, named for Zoroaster Temple that was named by George Wharton James in 1902 for a Persian religious leader. James described it as "a pillar of fire." It is easily visible from the Trail of Time.

My rock type is an igneous rock. I am a granodiorite showing some magma mixing. I have a strong layering due to deformation and I am sometimes called gneiss (pronounced "nice"), a name I like.

My age is 1,740 ± 2 million years old based on radiometric dating of my zircon crystals.[53]

My story: My parent magmas were mantle melts; I was intruded into the crust as a granodiorite pluton. During the Yavapai orogeny, I was squeezed and my minerals rotated perpendicular to the squeezing direction into a strong layering (foliation). My outcrops can be seen north of the river between Bright Angel Canyon and Clear Creek. Long after I became a rock in the deep crust, I was brought to Earth's surface by erosion and I formed islands in the Cambrian Tapeats seaway 500 million years ago that were not covered up with sediment until Bright Angel time. Today, the Colorado River is carving through me and making a spectacular steep-walled part of the Upper Granite Gorge.

1,740 Ma

Vishnu Schist: nature and nurture!

Vishnu Schist, 1,750 million years old. By nature I was a sedimentary rock, but I was changed by metamorphism. The rectangular area needs a closer look.

Look closely and use the magnifying glass on your phone if you have one; the red minerals (squarish and hexagonal shapes) are garnet and the fibrous minerals are sillimanite (blue), two high temperature (~ 650 degrees Celsius) metamorphic minerals. The quartz veins (yellow) reflect metamorphic fluids frozen in the rock.

Folding rotated my initially horizontal bedding to near vertical in this outcrop along the river far below us.

My formal name is Vishnu Schist, named for Vishnu Temple that was named by Clarence Dutton in 1882 who said it looked like a Hindu Temple.

My rock type is a metamorphic rock but I was initially a clay-bearing sandstone. My original composition influenced my metamorphism such that the aluminum in the clays helped garnet and sillimanite to grow.

My age is 1,750 ± 2 million years old as dated by the U-Pb radiometric method on zircons from an ash layer that Brahma and I are interlayered with. I contain grains over 3 billion years old that made up part of my sediments.[56]

My story: I have had a long journey. My nature is as a sedimentary rock. I was originally deposited in the ocean on a steep slope in a trench setting. Not long after I became a sedimentary rock I underwent major changes. I got carried to over 20 km deep in the Earth[50] by thrust faults and was heated to about 600 degrees Celsius (over 1,000 degrees Fahrenheit- twice your hottest oven setting) and I resided there for millions of years between 1.71 and 1.70 billion years ago. I did not melt, but new minerals grew, including the garnets you see. I was brought to 10 km depths about 1.68 billion years ago, and got all the way back to the surface by Bass's time, 1.25 billion years ago. Then I was buried again by 4 km of Grand Canyon Supergroup sedimentary rock. Up and down!, I yo-yoed back to the surface by erosion about 500 million years ago, then down I went again under 3 km of overlying flat layers. The river started carving down through me about 2 million years ago. I remember my nature, but my nurture was important too. I'll remain a metamorphic rock until I finally get eroded into sediment again.

1,745 Ma

Brahma Schist: same nurture, different nature.

Brahma Schist, 1,750 million years old.

Pillow basalts in Lower Granite Gorge were erupted under water then were deformed during the Yavapai orogeny.

My formal name is Brahma Schist of the Granite Gorge Metamorphic Suite. I was named by John Maxon for Brahma Temple that was named by Francois Matthes and approved by the U.S. Geological Survey in 1906.

My rock type is a metamorphic rock, but I was originally an igneous rock, a basalt. I was metamorphosed to an amphibole biotite schist (some call me amphibolite).

My age is $1,750 \pm 2$ million years old based on a U-Pb zircon date on a layer of ash I am interlayered with; this is the same age as Vishnu because we were deposited as interlayered sediment and lava flows.

My story: I was not laid down as a sedimentary rock like Vishnu and instead was a basaltic lava flow that erupted under water. When my magma entered the seawater, you can imagine the steam and turbulent explosions. The outsides of my flow quickly crystallized but the insides kept flowing on the seabed through insulated tubes to form pillow basalt, as shown above. The "pillow" shapes have been changed by deformation, but you can still make out the chilled rinds of the tubes. I had very different compositions than Rama and Vishnu and my new minerals that grew during metamorphism were mostly needles of hornblende, an amphibole. I was collected as a boulder from within the Colorado River in the Middle Granite Gorge, as you can see from how well I am polished.

1,750 Ma

Rama Schist: same journey, different nature.

Rama Schsit, 1,750 million years old. Once you sketch it, you see it. Most of my rock is a dark fine-grained metavolcanic rock called metarhyolite. The dikes and veins came later, about 1.7 billion years ago.

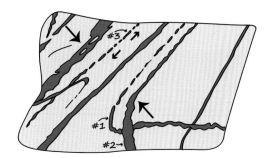

Sketch it to see it; early dikes (#1) are folded and cross cut by later ones (#2) that are less folded. Some dikes were stretched so thin they are now just one feldspar crystal wide (#3). The pegmatite dikes formed during metamorphism when the Rama metarhyolite was partially melting. Arrows indicate directions of shortening and extension during plate collisions.

My formal name is Rama Schist of the Granite Gorge Metamorphic Suite.

My rock type is a metamorphic rock, a quartz-feldspar schist, but I started out as a volcanic rock, a rhyolite.

My age is about 1,755 million years on the Trail of Time because I underlie Brahma in some places, but I am also interlayed U-Pb radiometric dating of zircons from different locations where I crop out give a range of ages from 1,751 ± 16 to 1,741 ± 1 indicating that there are several ages of volcanics in the basement rocks.

My story: Different types of lava were being erupted in the magmatic arc where I originated. Lava flows were interlayered with layers of sediment (Vishnu). I had the same long metamorphic journey as Brahma and Vishnu, my two sibling basement layers. I was initially more silica-rich and more explosive as young lava than Brahma. Once I was buried to 20-km depths, my minerals changed shape but no fancy metamorphic minerals, like Vishnu's garnets, grew. Instead, I started to partially melt and thin dikes of new granite material filled cracks. Some of them were folded before others formed — can you see and sketch out the dikes and their relative ages?

1,755 Ma

Elves Chasm gneiss tells the ups and downs of the oldest rocks.

Elves Chasm gneiss – 1,840 million years old. I am the oldest known rock unit in southwestern U.S.A.

Sketch it to see it: the dark gabbro (purple) enclaves were like oil droplets in water and couldn't quit mix with the granodiorite (gd) melts when I first crystallized; then we were intruded by the zoned pegmatite (red) in an opening crack about 100 million years later. You can see a gneissic foliation (lines) that aligned my minerals.

My formal name type is Elves Chasm gneiss (pronounced "nice"). The white vein is a much younger pegmatite with nice zoning — probably about 1.7 billion years old.

My rock type is a granodiorite.

My age is 1,840 ± 1 million years old[53] (very precise!). I am 95% sure that my birthday is within one step on the Trail of Time of where they placed me.

My story: My rocks are remnants of a magmatic arc system that pre-dated all the others by about 100 million years. I am the true basement within Grand Canyon's basement, nearly half as old as the Earth herself. I've had my ups and downs, hot times, and cold times as I made the journey to the deep crust and back. As a youngster, I was a magma (that was a hot time), then I turned into an igneous rock as my magma cooled deep in the Earth. My first trip to the Earth's surface was in time for Rama, Brahma, and Vishnu to be deposited as sedimentary and volcanic layers on top of me 1,750 million years ago. Then we were all buried to depths of about 20 km (12 miles) and were changed by heat and pressure into metamorphic rocks. I was deep in the Vishnu Mountains then and, as the mountains were gradually eroded away I came nearer the surface again. I had a lot of small ups and downs from 1,250 to 70 million years ago, as sedimentary layers were deposited and then partially eroded again and again above me. An exciting thing happened to me starting about 6 million years ago when the Colorado River cut down through the layers above me. These days, in the bottom of Grand Canyon, the river flows over my outcrops carrying sand and boulders that smooth and sculpt me (Ahhh).

1,840 Ma

The Making of the Trail of Time Geoscience Exhibition (1995-2010)

"You can read it in a book, but your eyes glaze over. It's better in little bits along the trail."
Quote from a visitor during prototype testing.

History of the Trail of Time Project.[57,58]

1995   Karl Karlstrom (UNM) and Mike Williams (UMass) conceived the idea of a scaled geologic walking trail and presented it to the Park Interpretation Division.

2001   Karl Karlstrom and Laura Crossey received a first planning grant from the National Science Foundation and held a workshop involving university leads, an advisory board, and Park officials.

2002   The University of New Mexico and Grand Canyon National Park entered into an agreement to develop the Trail of Time.

2003   Planning meeting at the Park for discussion of Trail of Time location and design.

2004   Phase 1 formative evaluation of a prototype Trail of Time by Selinda Research Associates and Park visitors.

2006   2.3 $M funding obtained from the National Science Foundation Informal Science Education Program; Trail of Time planning meeting held at South Rim of Grand Canyon.

2007   On-site formative testing of trail markers and temporary signs by Selinda Research Associates; cognition studies at ASU of Million Year Trail scale changes

2008   On-site formative testing of trail markers, waysides, and the "time zero" portal conducted by Selinda Research Associates and the Trail of Time team.

2009   Main Trail markers were installed between Grand Canyon Village and Yavapai Geology Museum; final on-site formative testing of portals, waysides, and viewing tubes conducted by Selinda Research Associates and the Trail of Time team.

2009   Grand Canyon rocks for the entry portals were collected by raft on the Colorado River.

2010   Final exhibit rocks for the plinths were collected along the Colorado River; waysides, portals, exhibit rocks, and viewing tubes were installed.

2010   Grand Opening ribbon cutting ceremony and Geoscience Education Symposium on "New Approaches to Geoscience Education in the National Park System."

Grand Canyon National Park officials and the university project leads cut the ribbon to officially open the Trail of Time.
L to R: Park Superintendent Steve Martin, Dr. Laura Crossey, Dr. Karl Karlstrom, Chief of the Division of Interpretation Judy Hellmich-Bryan, Dr. Steven Semken, Ryan Crow, and Dr. Michael Williams.

On October 13, 2010, the Trail of Time was officially dedicated with a ribbon-cutting ceremony. This was the highlight of the annual Earth Week celebration at Grand Canyon National Park.

The Project Team.

The Trail of Time project involved a collaboration among academics, the National Science Foundation, and the National Park Service for the dissemination of scientific research to the public.

University Project Team

Professor Karl Karlstrom, project lead, ToT conceiver, Grand Canyon researcher, University of New Mexico.
Professor Laura Crossey, co-lead, geology research and geoscience education, University of New Mexico.
Professor Steven Semken, ethnogeologist and geoscience education specialist, Arizona State University.
Professor Michael Williams, ToT conceiver and geology researcher, University of Massachusetts.
Ryan Crow, PhD student, Grand Canyon geology researcher, graphic design illustrations, and overall project mainstay, University of New Mexico, presently with U.S. Geological Survey.

Grand Canyon National Park Team

Judy Hellmich-Bryan, Chief of the Division of Interpretation and Resource Education.
Carl Bowman and Ellen Seeley, Branch Chiefs for Exhibits and Media.

Research and Evaluation Team

Dr. Deborah Perry, Dr. Eric Gyllenhaal, and Diane White of Selinda Research Associates.
Dr. Marcella Wells of Wells Resources, and the Trail of Time team.
Dr. Jeff Dodick, Hebrew University of Jerusalem, cognition of geologic time and change.

Design and Fabrication Team

Jim Sell Design: Jim Sell, Sue Sell, Matt Blakely, Brian Williamson, Mickey Schilling (artwork).
Dr. Marcella Wells, project management.
Rock & Company, fabrication.

Laurie Crossey and Karl Karlstrom

Ryan Crow

Mike Williams

Steve Semken

Carl Bowman

Ellen Seeley and Judy Hellmich-Bryan

Deborah Perry

Eric Gyllenhaal

The Making of the Trail of Time

Audiences.

Over six million people visit Grand Canyon each year. It is difficult to imagine any place in the world better suited to reach such a huge and diverse audience on themes of geology. All ages, nationalities, and ethnic groups are represented. Surveys show that 68% of these visitors take self-guided walks on the rim trail and 62% visit Yavapai Point. Thus, conservatively, 3 million people walk at least part of the Trail of Time each year. Your own goals and interests draw you to the Park, geology interest awakens, and the Trail of Time uses this opportunity to enhance your geologic understanding.

Family groups: About 30% of the travel parties include children under age 18. Often some member of the group (often the kids) leads group questions and conversations about abstract ideas. The combination of movement along the rim trail, rocks to touch, view tubes to interact with, and short bits of new information from wayside panels, as well as the constant time markers in the pavement, hold the interest of family groups and stimulate new ideas and discussions.

Laypeople with an interest in geology: About 41% of the visitors to Grand Canyon are repeat visitors, and many also visit nearby Parks. Many Grand Canyon visitors also visit Zion, Bryce Canyon, the Painted Desert, Petrified Forest, and/or Monument Valley. These laypeople with an interest in geology develop their own expertise about the geology of the Southwest and are a receptive audience for the Trail of Time.

International visitors: Most international visitor groups have at least one member who speaks English. The short, simple messages with explanatory graphics on the wayside panels tested well with our international visitors. One can now hear geology discussed in many languages along the Trail.

Science literacy: Understanding Earth (the science of Geology) is ever more important as human societies flourish on our planet of limited resources. Education and research on deep time, Earth's record of climate and environmental change, natural resources, and the interactions of humans in the Earth system are urgent topics for both formal and informal science education and public science literacy. This exhibit promotes science literacy and innovative approaches in effective geoscience education and interpretation.

The Knowledge Hierarchy.

The Knowledge Hierarchy is useful in all types of educational settings.[59] It focuses on the learning journeys that people are on. For example, one hierarchy that emerged during our evaluation of visitors' understandings of the time significance of Grand Canyon rocks showed a six-step learning journey.[60] Rather than targeting any particular level, the overall goal of the Trail of Time is to help visitors move up the hierarchy from whatever their level of entry may be.

Time Significance of Grand Canyon's Rocks: This hierarchy looks at visitors' understanding of the time significance of the rocks layers and of the un-layered igneous and metamorphic rock bodies that occur in the deepest parts of the Canyon. The ideas here may seem complex, especially at the upper levels of the hierarchy. However, they represent the basic intellectual "tool kit" that geologists use to establish the geologic history of Grand Canyon.

Level 0: "I don't know, and I don't care." Respondents at this level had little prior knowledge about and/or interest in the rocks as evidence of past times, although they often were impressed by their beauty and shape.

Level 1: "I don't know, but I'm curious." These respondents did not know much about the time significance of the rocks they saw in the canyon, but they were curious and wanted to know more. As they explored the Park, they had been wondering how old the rocks were, but they did not find or develop answers to their questions.

Level 2: Some knowledge, but it's incomplete or incorrect. These respondents were interested enough that they had developed a theory or hypothesis about the ages of the rocks in the Canyon. Some respondents believed all the rocks were less than 10,000 years old. Other respondents' understandings were based on scientific ideas or suppositions, but were incomplete or incorrect — such as young respondents who thought they had found dinosaur claws in the Park (but had really found triangular fragments of Kaibab limestone).

Level 3: Basic understanding of the time significance of layered rocks in the Canyon. Respondents on this level:

a) Realized that the rock layers in the Canyon walls were widespread and could be seen all around the Canyon's walls. (In other words, they had at least a basic understanding of the concept of bedrock.)

b) Realized each layer of bedrock formed at a certain time, and thus any rock, plucked from the Canyon and placed on a plinth could be given an "age."

c) Realized that rock layers of different ages could be recognized and named throughout the park by matching them to cliffs, slopes, and benches.

Respondents who spent some time at the Horizontal Layers wayside and viewing tubes often gained enough knowledge that they approached this level of understanding.

Level 4: Deeper understanding of the time significance of the Canyon's rocks. Respondents on this level had a basic understanding of some geological principles. For instance, they understood one or more of these ideas:

a) older rocks were deeper in the Canyon (law of superposition);

b) each rock layer is continuous around the Canyon's walls (lateral continuity);

c) each layer is (about) the same age everywhere in the Park; and

d) basement rocks, although not layered, had time significance because they can be directly dated.

Many respondents who reached this level probably did so gradually as they accumulated new understandings along the Trail, but most were at this level because they came to the Trail with this understanding, perhaps having studied geology in a formal setting.

Level 5: Familiar with the major rock units in the Park and their time significance. These respondents knew many of the major rock units by name and knew in general terms when the major layers were formed.

Level 6: Sophisticated understanding of Grand Canyon geology and its global significance. These respondents think about the rocks like geologists do. Respondents at this level understood the concept of the unconformities and their significance as "gaps" in the geologic record of the Park.

Cognition research about geologic time and processes.

The Trail of Time exhibition continues to provide opportunities for research in public cognition of deep time and geology. Some research suggests that spatial visualization and temporal learning may be correlated. Much less certain is the effectiveness of kinesthetic reinforcement of temporal and spatial learning. Our research has found that both the tactile learning, for example touching the rocks, and the group learning that accompanies the physical activities of the Trail of Time walk are effective complements to geoscience learning and motivation. The research and evaluation process worked to identify and characterize preconceptions related to deep time and geologic processes and assess the effectiveness of our timeline analogy and various ancillary materials in correcting misconceptions. The results of this research are useful for many other types of informal geoscience education exhibitions. Additional research has been conducted on the effectiveness of virtual fieldtrips compared to actual fieldtrips for geology cognition, with the finding that each has separate strengths and that both learning and motivation benefit from the combination.

Steve Semken, Laurie Crossey, and Karl Karlstrom evaluating prototype signs.

Ethnogeoscience.

This exhibition was planned to be both "culturally sensitive" and to help develop the field of ethnogeoscience.[61,62] The latter researches the concept that Native American cultures have an extensive scientific knowledge base that has developed from long-term interaction with the landscape, water, resources, and climate change. The homelands of many Native American nations including the Havasupai, Hualapai, Hopi, Southern Paiute, and Navajo, adjoin the Grand Canyon, and ethnogeoscience figures prominently in their cultural knowledge systems. Native American content is traditionally presented in an archaeological context within Park exhibits and museums, which do not indicate that such knowledge systems are evolving, relevant, scientific, and still in use by a significant number of the permanent inhabitants of the lands surrounding the Park.

Dr. Steven Semken

Evaluation and Assessment.

Will visitors understand that they are walking an abstract timeline?
How do we use the time markers to maintain visitor's interest but not detract from the awesome canyon views?
What is the best way to write large numbers so they are understood by the most people?

These are just a few of the many questions that were investigated through prototype testing with visitors on and off-site and reviews of existing research from a variety of fields. Selinda Research Associates compiled evaluation briefs on each element of the Trail of Time; these are available online to help with other informal geoscience exhibitions developed in the future (www.TOT@unm.edu). The crucial early prototype trail consisted of 3000 brass-colored marks taped at one meter intervals to the paved rim trail to determine if visitors would understand the concept of the trail as an abstract timeline. Although timelines have been used in museums and exhibitions, this is a difficult concept for casual visitors, but our research showed that visitors did grasp this concept. The use of small markers at one meter intervals with larger markers at 10 meter intervals proved to be enough to keep the idea of a timeline in visitors' minds while not being so distracting that visitors would be looking at the ground instead of the views.

Prototype testing involved 3000 markers taped to the trail and rocks on plywood plinths.

Most visitors freely gave their opinions on the Trail of Time and helped with the evaluation. Their feedback was immediately incorporated in the signs and then retested with more visitors in a process called rapid prototyping.

Prototype portal sign with text changed during rapid prototyping to reflect visitor feedback.

Budget and funding.

Funding from the National Science Foundation

University of New Mexico – concept and content development,
   project management, and University overhead costs ---------------------- $475,000
Arizona State University – concept and content development,
   University overhead costs --- $200,000
River trips to collect and transport rocks, installation of markers ------------ $150,000
Evaluation and cognition research --------------------------------------- $350,000
Project Design -- $280,000
Bronze fabrication for trail markers ------------------------------------- $125,000
Cutting and polishing rocks, fabrication of plinths,
   installation of rocks on plinths and portals -------------------------------- $570,000
Fabrication of wayside panels --- $100,000
Symposium costs -- $50,000

       Total NSF Contributions------------------------------------ **$2,300,000**

In-kind contributions from Grand Canyon National Park

Helicopter support for rock collection ----------------------------------- $15,000
Trail crew support -- $10,000
River trip support -- $15,000
Printing of Trail of Time materials -------------------------------------- $10,000
Interpretive staff participation -- $20,000
Grand opening, symposium costs -- $10,000
Repaving of trail --- $100,000

      Total in-kind support from Grand Canyon National Park ---- **$180,000**

Helicopter support was provided by the Park; at times involving both the Park helicopter and a heavy lift helicopter (in the air in this photo).

The Park, University of New Mexico, and Arizona River Runners contributed rafts and boatmen for transport of Trail of Time rocks.

Components of the Trail of Time — The Rock Portals.

The Trail of Time can be entered at different points — including the east end, west end, and a middle point where a connecting trail from the Park Headquarters meets the canyon rim. This "porous" trail presented both a design and interpretive challenge. The solution involved entry portals with messages on each side appropriate for the approaching visitor.

The base of the portals that represent Grand Canyon's basement rocks were collected from the Idaho Springs Formation of Colorado, which is similar in age and rock type to Vishnu Schist. They were cut by a computer-driven rock saw by Rock & Company in Brighton, Colorado. The layered rocks were collected along the river in Grand Canyon, cut to scale, and constructed in a veneer that shows the rock layers and their erosion profile. The tilted supergroup layers are shown at half thickness relative to the upper flat lying layers.

Portal design is striking with actual rocks from the canyon layers in a to-scale touchable geologic column. Visitors are drawn to the portals and immediately run their hands down the layers. The rock portals enclose a uniquely shaped exhibit panel with a large clear map of the trail with the current location clearly marked. Large print and three short sentences of information help visitors quickly grasp the message. The graphic of people on the trail reinforces the purpose of the trail, especially for international visitors and children.

Components of the Trail of Time — Trail Markers.

Research showed that using the word million or billion is preferred to writing numbers with many zeros. Numbers in the billions could have been written as 1.5 billion or 1,500 million. Both systems were tested and it was found least confusing to stick with millions of years.

The bronze trail markers provide continuity to all the segments of the trail. The bronze disks were set into an existing asphalt rim trail. The markers are the feature that makes the trail a timeline. This is a difficult concept for many visitors so the wording on the trail markers was crucial. Several different designs were tested. We found it was important that the word timeline be on the marker. It was found that numbered markers every meter were not needed on the Main segment of trail. The simple brass disks at one meter intervals with numbered markers every ten meters were enough to capture visitors' attention, but not distract from the canyon views. However, on the Million Year segment where time accelerates, each meter is marked with a numbered disk. On the Early Earth segment, in an area that is less developed, only the ten-meter numbered disks were installed.

2,500 markers were installed by Karl Karlstrom, Laura Crossey, Ryan Crow, and the Trail of Time team. The Main Trail is marked every 10 million years with these larger markers. Omission of the comma in 1,680 was a fabrication error.

Vandalism or creative additions? Soon after the installation, some visitors discovered that pennies just fit into the recession in the "ones" markers. Within months, every marker had its own penny. We consider it an enhancement, and the labor was free!

Fraction of billions or thousands of millions? Our testing showed that thousands of millions allowed visitors to grasp the idea that the numbers were increasing by 10 million years.[60]

Components of the Trail of Time — Wayside Panels.

The seventeen waysides have large graphics and little text. Originally, we thought that most visitors would read the large headings, then more text could provide for those who wanted more information. However, our research showed that text-heavy waysides were not read at all. Visitor input during prototype testing was used to determine the final text that was designed to be conversational. We observe that visitors sometimes walk by the signs as if not seeing it, only to have one of the group recite the conversational heading to the others farther down the trail, saying: "Did you know that…Grand Canyon is 6 million years old?"

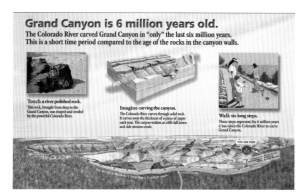

Each wayside panel includes a map along the bottom edge that clearly indicates where in time along the timeline the wayside is located and the distances to the east and west ends of the trail. On the Main Trail of Time, the map also includes a geologic column of canyon rock layers and the location of that layer in the canyon walls. This helps relate the abstract concept of a horizontal timeline to the vertical distribution of rocks in the canyon, a recognized challenge of the exhibit.

Components of the Trail of Time – View Tubes.

View tubes have been used in many National Parks and other outdoor settings to direct visitor attention. These tubes do not magnify, but help focus on one small part of the large scene. View tubes at two different heights allow children, individuals in wheelchairs, and adults of all heights to comfortably use them. Both view tubes are focused on the same aspect. Between the high and low view tubes is a photo showing the scene before the visitor with the focus of the view tube clearly marked.

The Trail of Time has eight carefully selected view tube locations.

Views through the view tubes — east to west

48 yrs - Colorado River
190,000 yrs - Uinkaret volcanoes
271 Ma – Kaibab Formation on both rims
275 Ma – Top four rock layers
584 Ma – Bright Angel Shale layer
1,010 Ma – Hakatai Shale layer of the Supergroup Rocks
1,162 Ma – Great Unconformity
1,720 Ma – Vishnu Schist in the Basement Rocks

Evaluation results made it clear that the tubes were popular and needed to be available at different heights. At left, a girl on tip-toes is stretching to look through a prototype view tube.

Components of the Trail of Time — Rocks on Plinths.

For many visitors, the rocks are the most important part of the Trail of Time. From children to grandparents, visitors touch the faces of the rocks and remark about touching an object that old. Some photograph every rock. The combination of weathered and cut faces gives a sense of looking into the rock. Each rock was selected by the UNM team on raft trips down the Colorado River. Collecting the specimens was a major undertaking involving heavy-lifting. Six tons of rocks were taken through Grand Canyon on rafts. Another three tons of rocks were removed by the park service helicopter and a special heavy-lift helicopter. The rocks were then cut and polished. Limestone plinths (Indiana Limestone) were cut, shaped, and trucked on-site. Each plinth includes the name of the rock its age, and the Trail of Time symbol on the angled face.

Geologists selected each rock from places that would not leave an impact. They argued about which specimens revealed the most beautiful and representative features for each rock unit.

An important element was the words "Touch me" on the corner of each plinth. This wording was tested and "Touch me" proved to encourage visitors to touch the rocks whereas, perhaps from pre-conditioning, visitors incorrectly read the words "Please touch" to mean "Please DON"T touch."

Three tons of rocks were collected by helicopter in daisy chain-type loads like this one.

Six tons of rocks were collected on rafts. This raft and boatman were donated by Arizona River Runners – Thanks ARR!

Out-takes — early concepts, ideas, and some bloopers.

This 1994 drawing accompanied a formal proposal to the Park. Our 1995 concept letter proposed: *"It can bring the message about geologic time, geologic history, and science in general to a larger number of people, and especially children.... The goal is not just to describe the history but to provide an interactive, multi-level earth science course that is enjoyable for people of all ages and backgrounds... to make the best, most effective interpretive scientific display/program/activity in the world.... It seems fitting to design and implement such a display at Grand Canyon, a pre-eminent geologic wonder and one of the most visited parks in the country."*

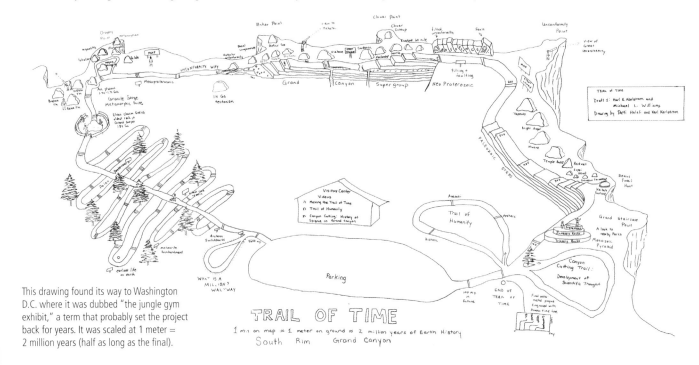

This drawing found its way to Washington D.C. where it was dubbed "the jungle gym exhibit," a term that probably set the project back for years. It was scaled at 1 meter = 2 million years (half as long as the final).

2002 Ideas.

Rectangular markers would have been harder to install and less durable.

View to Permian strata and Mesozoic rocks of Zion National Park

The main idea for the Trail of Time has always been the marked trail itself. One possibility for marking is shown here: numbered markers each 10 million years, inset markers every meter.

Potential exhibits for the Trail

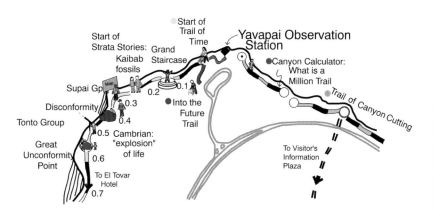

Start of Strata Stories: Kaibab fossils

Start of Trail of Time

Grand Staircase

Yavapai Observation Station

Canyon Calculator: What is a Million Trail

Supai Gp

Map

Trail of Canyon Cutting

Disconformity

0.2

0.1

Into the Future Trail

Tonto Group

0.3

0.4

Great Unconformity Point

0.5 Cambrian: "explosion" of life

To Visitor's Information Plaza

0.6

To El Tovar Hotel

0.7

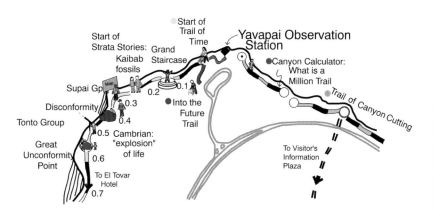

Looking Deeper into Geology – this section lets you apply and test your knowledge.

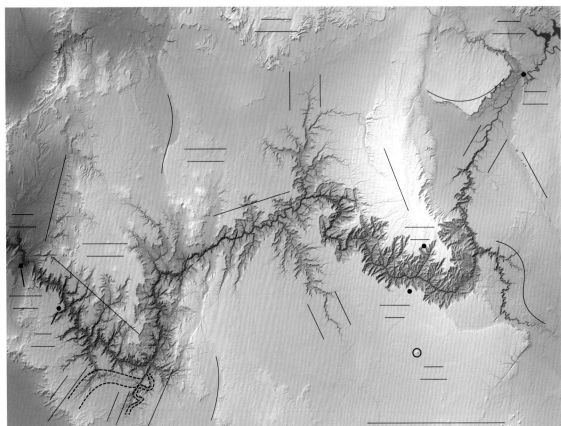

Match these names and numbers to their places on the map. See page 24 for help.

1. Aubrey Cliffs
2. Eastern G.C. segment
3. Echo Cliffs
4. Grand Staircase
5. Grand Wash Cliffs
6. Havasu Canyon
7. Hindu paleocanyon
8. Hurricane Cliffs
9. Hurricane G.C. segment
10. Kaibab Uplift
11. Kanab Canyon
12. Lake Powell
13. Lake Mead
14. Lees Ferry
15. Little Colorado River
16. Marble Canyon
17. Muav Gorge
18. North Rim
19. Peach Springs paleocanyon
20. Pearce Ferry
21. Red Butte
22. San Francisco volcanic field
23. Shivwits Plateau
24. Sky Walk
25. South Rim
26. Uinkaret Plateau
27. Vermillion Cliffs
28. Western G.C. segment

Geologic Evolution of Grand Canyon at a glance.

1,840 to 1,750 million years ago, volcanic islands formed and began to collide.

Vishnu Mountains

20 km (12 miles) deep

1,720 to 1,660 million years ago, the continent was welded together.

The Great Nonconformity

1,660 to 1,255 million years ago, the Vishnu mountains were eroded flat.

1,255 to 1,100 million years ago, the Unkar Group of the Grand Canyon Supergroup was deposited.

780 to 729 million years ago, the Chuar Group of the Grand Canyon Supergroup was deposited.

The Great Angular Unconformity

729 to 530 million years ago, the area was eroded flat again. The Great Unconformity is where Tonto Group rests on eroded Precambrian rocks.

530 to 500 million years ago, the lower flat layers were deposited to form the Cambrian Tonto Group.

Mesozoic strata

Paleozoic strata

385 to 80 million years ago, the upperflat layers were deposited; first the Paleozoic then the Mesozoic layers.

80 to 20 million years ago, the region was uplifted high above sea level and began to erode again.

6 million years ago the Grand Canyon started to be carved and it is still being carved today!

How geologists tell time.

Understanding the Park's resources is linked to understanding the interaction of different timescales. This page helps you understand how geologists "tell time." Two ways of telling time are well known to everyone– relative time is ordering what came first and what came next. The sedimentary layers in Grand Canyon are good example of this method — the ones on top had to be laid down after the ones below. The geologic time scale on page 121 was constructed using relative age of index fossils in sedimentary successions like this around the world. Geologists found that older fossils, from lower layers in a given section, were very different that those in upper layers due to evolution of life on Earth. "Absolute" time is added using a variety of naturally decaying radioactive elements that serve as "clocks" and can measure when, in years, an event happened. The term "numeric" might be better than "absolute" because geochronologists continually refine techniques such that numeric ages change slightly, uncertainties get less, and sometimes fossil boundaries shift by several million years. In sedimentary rocks, we rely on the ages of datable ash layers found interbedded with the layers; or we can get an age on the sand grains and bracket the age of a sandstone by knowing that it must have been deposited after its youngest dated grain formed. The time of crystallization of an igneous rock from a melt can often be directly dated, for example using the mineral zircon. The information in this guide is all about time — it is up-to-date as of 2018. We look forward to slight changes in the future as the science gains new knowledge, but the basic age framework is well known, tested and re-tested by applying multiple methods. The ages for all Grand Canyon's rocks are summarized on pages 135–136.

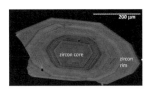

Geochronology — when a rock formed. Igneous rocks are dated with the mineral zircon which crystallizes in the magma when the rock forms. Zircons contains two different parent isotopes of uranium that decay at different rates to two different daughter isotopes of lead. They generally remain a closed system so these two independent dates cross check each other.

Thermochronology — when a rock cooled. Apatite crystals record the cooling history of a rock from 110 to 40 degrees Celsius as erosion brings the rock up closer to the surface. This is equivalent to tracking its journey from 4 km depths to 1 km depth as the Mesozoic strata were eroded away.

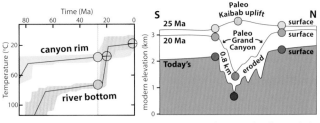

Thermochronology — tracking past landscapes: Two samples were taken from Today's surface on opposite rims of eastern Grand Canyon (green dots) and one at the bottom (purple dot). Their apatite cooling histories[63] show that, at 25 Ma, they were at different temperatures, hence different depths below the paleo Kaibab uplift (dashed line). By 20 Ma, the samples were the same temperature, hence the same depth, indicating that a paleo Grand Canyon had been carved in this segment (20 Ma solid line). Since 20 Ma, an additional ~0.8 km of erosion occurred, deepening eastern Grand Canyon.

The Geologic Timescale then and now.

The geologic timescale is one of the most fundamental contributions of the science of geology. Geologists discovered that sets of distinctive index fossils occurred in the same relative order in layered sequences all over the world. This gave rise to the relative time scale of geologic Eras, Periods, and Epochs as shown. Since the discovery of radioactivity and the application of numerous radiometric "clocks," we now know the age of the Earth to be 4.567 billion years, and geologists continually refine the timescale with precise dates on ash beds found interlayered with sedimentary rocks above and below key fossil transitions.[34]

Eon	Era	Period		Epoch	Age (millions of years)
Phanerozoic	Cenozoic	Quaternary	Neogene	Holocene (Recent)	0.01
				Pleistocene	2.6
				Pliocene	5
				Miocene	23
		Tertiary	Paleogene	Oligocene	34
				Eocene	56
				Paleocene	66
	Mesozoic	Cretaceous			145
		Jurassic			201
		Triassic			252
	Paleozoic	Permian		*Epochs are defined for each period although those of the Cenozoic Era are most commonly used. Epoch names in most periods are indicated by the adjectives "Lower", "Middle", and "Upper" with the period name; e.g. Upper Devonian Epoch. Stage names, within epochs, refer to fossil groups alive at various times.*	299
		Carboniferous	Pennsylvanian		323
			Mississippian		359
		Devonian			419
		Silurian			444
		Ordovician			485
		Cambrian			541
Precambrian	Proterozoic	Neoproterozoic			1000
		Mesoproterozoic			1600
		Paleoproterozoic			2500
	Archean	Neoarchean			2800
		Mesoarchean			3200
		Paleoarchean			3600
		Eoarchean			4560

Ages based on International Chronostratigraphic chart v. 2018/08 www.stratigraphy.org

The Kaibab Fossil Walk.

Find these Permian fossils near marker 3,150 on the Early Earth Trail, about 200 m (0.3 mile) west of Grand Canyon Village. Find and touch (but do not collect) fossils from animals that lived and died in the Permian oceans about 270 million years ago.

Look down at flat outcrops on both sides of the Trail and imagine the diverse marine life that lived and died in the muddy bottom waters of the Permian sea, 270 million years ago. These animals became entombed as fossils in the Kaibab Limestone. Most of the animals here were marine filter feeders. Geologists identify the groups of fossils found to understand past ecosystems and define biozones. Biozones from a given layer, like the Kaibab Limestone, can be correlated with rocks from around the world to help date rocks (see p. 120) and understand evolutionary changes and extinctions.

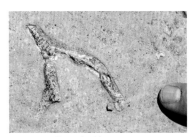

Branched bryozoan
Bryozoa

Common Name
Phylum
Genus species

Pseudofossil
Chert concretions in limestone

Fenestrate bryozoan
Bryozoa
Fenestella

Stem segments of crinoids
Echinodermata

Brachiopod
Brachiopoda
Derbyia sp.

Brachiopod
Brachiopoda
Meekella

Productide brachiopod
Brachiopoda
Penciculauris bassi

Little did the Permian creatures know that 95% of their species would die out 252 million years ago during the largest mass extinction, known as the Great Dying.[64] The Great Dying at the end of the Permian is the largest of the five mass extinctions in Earth's history. Trilobites, horn corals, and all of the brachiopods shown here went completely extinct. Clams, sponges, crinoids, and bryozoans went nearly extinct. One of the biggest changes was that clams, snails, and advanced corals came to dominate the seafloor instead of brachiopods, bryozoans, and crinoids. This extinction event was caused by massive volcanism in Siberia that caused changes in global climate and ocean chemistry.[65]

Sponge in chert nodule
Porifera

Horn coral
Cnidaria (Rugosa)

Spot the temples and towers and other features of the inner canyon. This is the widest and deepest part of Grand Canyon.

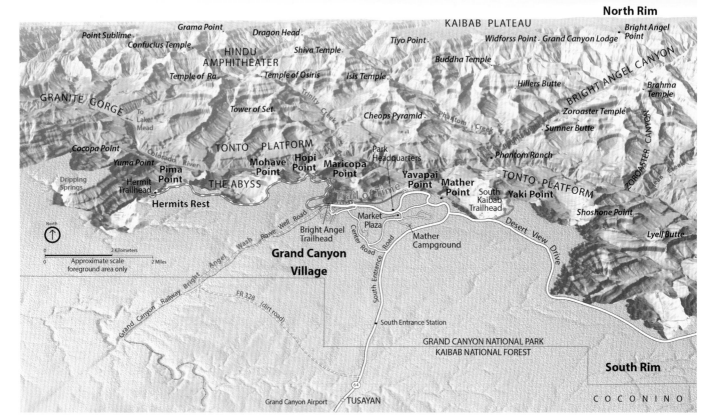

North Rim

KAIBAB PLATEAU

Point Sublime
Grama Point
Dragon Head
Tiyo Point
Widforss Point · Grand Canyon Lodge
Bright Angel Point

Confucius Temple
HINDU AMPHITHEATER
Shiva Temple
Buddha Temple

Temple of Ra
Temple of Osiris
Isis Temple
Hillers Butte
Brahma Temple

GRANITE GORGE
Tower of Set
Trinity Creek
Cheops Pyramid
Zoroaster Temple

To Lake Mead
Phantom Creek
Sumner Butte

Cocopa Point
Colorado River
TONTO PLATFORM
Park Headquarters
Phantom Ranch

Yuma Point
Mohave Point
Hopi Point
Maricopa Point
Yavapai Point
TONTO PLATFORM

Dripping Springs
Pima Point
THE ABYSS
Mather Point
South Kaibab Trailhead
Yaki Point

Hermit Trailhead
Trail of Time
Shoshone Point

Hermits Rest
Market Plaza
ZOROASTER CANYON

BRIGHT ANGEL CANYON

North

Bright Angel Trailhead
Mather Campground
Lyell Butte

2 Kilometers
0
0
2 Miles
Approximate scale foreground area only

Center Road
Desert View Drive

Grand Canyon Village

South Entrance Road

Rawe Well Road

Bright Angel Wash
Grand Canyon Railway
FR 328 (dirt road)

South Entrance Station

GRAND CANYON NATIONAL PARK
KAIBAB NATIONAL FOREST

South Rim

Grand Canyon Airport
64
TUSAYAN
C O C O N I N O

In eastern Grand Canyon, the Colorado River changes from its southerly course to a westerly course that enters the Granite Gorge and carves across the Kaibab Plateau.

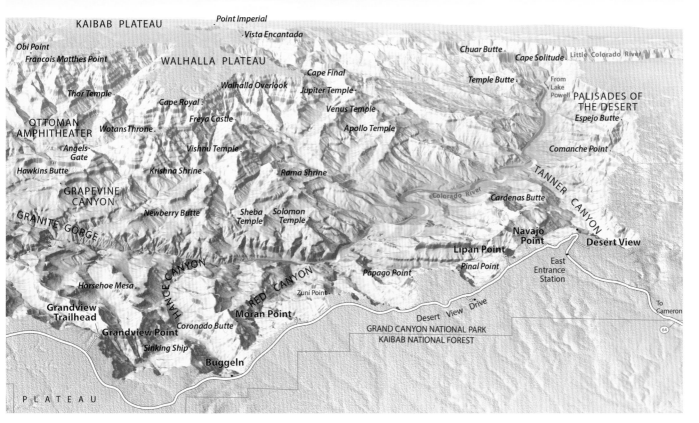

KAIBAB PLATEAU

Point Imperial

Vista Encantada

Obi Point

Francois Matthes Point

WALHALLA PLATEAU

Chuar Butte

Cape Solitude

Little Colorado River

Cape Final

Temple Butte

From Lake Powell

PALISADES OF THE DESERT

Thor Temple

Walhalla Overlook

Jupiter Temple

Cape Royal

Venus Temple

Espejo Butte

OTTOMAN AMPHITHEATER

Freya Castle

Wotans Throne

Apollo Temple

Comanche Point

Angels Gate

Vishnu Temple

Hawkins Butte

Krishna Shrine

Rama Shrine

TANNER CANYON

GRAPEVINE CANYON

Colorado River

Cardenas Butte

Newberry Butte

Sheba Temple

Solomon Temple

GRANITE GORGE

Navajo Point

Lipan Point

Desert View

Horsehoe Mesa

HANCE CANYON

RED CANYON

Papago Point

Pinal Point

East Entrance Station

Grandview Trailhead

Zuni Point

Desert View Drive

To Cameron

Grandview Point

Coronado Butte

Moran Point

GRAND CANYON NATIONAL PARK

KAIBAB NATIONAL FOREST

Sinking Ship

Buggeln

64

PLATEAU

Water is one of Grand Canyon's most precious resources.

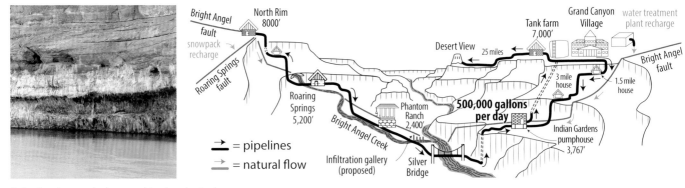

Native American peoples have sought and used natural resources of the Grand Canyon region for more than 10,000 years. Among other things, they needed plants for sandals and baskets, clay for pots, chert and obsidian for projectile points, salt for nutrition, minerals for dyes, caves for shelter and food storage, river terraces for farming, and building materials. Then, as now, water was one of the most precious resources.

Photo: NPS/Mark Lellouch

Water for growing South Rim communities from 1901 to 1927 was delivered by railroad.[66] In 1932, a pumphouse was built to lift 150,000 gallons per day of Indian Gardens spring water 3,200 feet (840 m) to the South Rim. From 1956-1966, a transcanyon water pipeline was built to transfer water, using gravity, from Roaring Springs (elevation 5,200 feet) 12.4 miles from near the North Rim to Indian Gardens (elevation 3,767 feet), then pumping it up to the South Rim (6,500 feet). This was an amazing engineering feat! In 1966, a flash flood along Bright Angel Creek wiped out about 40% of the pipeline. Since 2015, about 500,000 gallons per day are pumped to South Rim. But frequent leaks and breakage along the pipeline have led to new ideas. For example a well or infiltration gallery could collect Bright Creek water and pump it up from Phantom Ranch. Developing sustainable water supply and water quality for the region are urgent needs. This includes understanding potential impacts of uranium mining, of excess water withdrawal all around the Park, and of increasing tourism.

Grand Canyon's mineral resources have been mined for many years.

Native peoples used mineral resources too, but impacts of European settlers have been much greater. John Wesley Powell's 1871 expedition found traces of placer gold in Kanab Creek, causing a mini- gold rush. Other explorers and settlers found copper and asbestos. The names of 1880-1890s miners are well known because they also built the earliest hotels and trails: John Hance, William Bass, Dan Hogan, Louis Boucher (the Hermit), Pete Berry and Ralph Cameron. The mining endeavors did not pay off (except uranium) and more money was made from tourism.

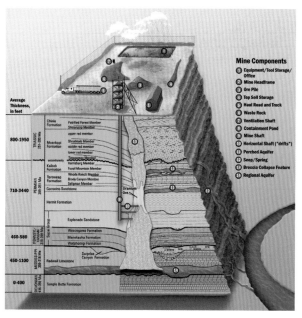

High grade uranium deposits occur in the Grand Canyon region, including the Orphan Mine near Maricopa Point and the Canyon Mine south of the Park.[67] They occur in breccia pipes which are vertical pipes formed as rock from overlying layers collapsed into caves of the Redwall Limestone. Mineralized fluids moving vertically through the pipes deposited uranium mainly at the level of the Hermit Formation.[68] Mining peaked in the 1980s but is still active. Potential future uranium mining provides tensions between mineral extraction and the need to preserve Park resources, including water quality. Mining relics from the Orphan Mine have been removed but the Canyon Mine is still active

Looking Deeper

Test your knowledge of the rock names and the sequence of geologic events at Grand Canyon. Note that red lines are unconformities and blue lines show water pathways.

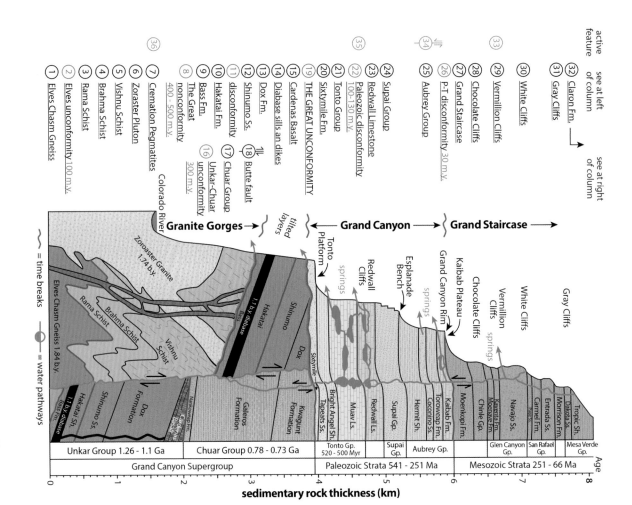

active feature

see at left of column

see at right of column

(32) Claron Fm.
(31) Gray Cliffs

(30) White Cliffs
(29) Vermillion Cliffs
(28) Chocolate Cliffs
(27) Grand Staircase
(26) P-T disconformity 30 m.y.
(25) Aubrey Group

(24) Supai Group
(23) Redwall Limestone
(22) Paleozoic disconformity 100-130 m.y.
(21) Tonto Group
(20) Sixtymile Fm.
(19) THE GREAT UNCONFORMITY

(16) Unkar-Chuar unconformity 300 m.y.
(17) Chuar Group
(18) Butte fault

(15) Cardenas Basalt
(14) Diabase sills an dikes
(13) Dox Fm.
(12) Shinumo Ss.
(11) disconformity
(10) Hakatai Fm.
(9) Bass Fm.
(8) The Great nonconformity 400 - 500 m.y.

(7) Cremation Pegmatites
(6) Zoroaster Pluton
(5) Vishnu Schist
(4) Brahma Schist
(3) Rama Schist
(2) Elves unconformity 100 m.y.
(1) Elves Chasm Gneiss

Granite Gorges → | tilted layers | ← Grand Canyon → | Grand Staircase →

Colorado River

Zoroaster Granite 1.74 b.y.

Elves Chasm Gneiss 1.84 b.y.
Rama Schist
Brahma Schist
Vishnu Schist
Hakatai
Shinumo
1.1 b.y. diabase Bass
Dox
Sixtymile
Tonto Platform
springs
Redwall Cliffs
Esplanade Bench
Chocolate Cliffs
Grand Canyon Rim
Kaibab Plateau
springs
springs
Vermillion Cliffs
White Cliffs
Gray Cliffs

Hakatai Sh.
Shinumo Ss.
Dox Formation
1.1 b.y diabase
Bass Formation
Cardenas Basalt
Nankoweap Formation
Galeros Formation
Kwagunt Formation
Tapeats Ss.
Bright Angel Sh.
Muav Ls.
Redwall Ls.
Supai Gp.
Hermit Sh.
Coconino Ss.
Toroweap Fm.
Kaibab Fm.
Moenkopi Fm.
Chinle Gp.
Moenave Fm.
Kayenta Fm.
Navajo Ss.
Carmel Fm.
Entrada Ss.
Morrison Fm.
Dakota Ss.
Tropic Sh.

Unkar Group 1.26 - 1.1 Ga | Chuar Group 0.78 - 0.73 Ga | Tonto Gp. 520 - 500 Myr | Supai Gp. | Aubrey Gp. | Glen Canyon Gp. | San Rafael Gp. | Mesa Verde Gp.

Grand Canyon Supergroup | Paleozoic Strata 541 - 251 Ma | Mesozoic Strata 251 - 66 Ma | Age

~ = time breaks   ●—● = water pathways

sedimentary rock thickness (km)

Rock names, time gaps, and geologic events oldest (#1) at bottom, youngest (#36) at top.

36. The Colorado River is carving Grand Canyon deeper at about 0.15 mm per year.

35. N-rim springs of the Redwall-Muav (RM) aquifer provide drinking water to the South Rim.

34. Springs flow from the Coconino and Kaibab (C) aquifers and groundwater follows faults.

33. Springs from the Navajo Sandstone (N-aquifer) is important for nearby regions.

32. The Claron Formation in the Bryce Canyon region records 50 Ma old lakebeds.

31. The Gray Cliffs of Dakota Sandstone were originally beach sands of an interior seaway.

30. The White Cliffs of upper Navajo Sandstone were deposited as vast sand dune fields.

29. Vermillion Cliffs of Glen Canyon Group form the redbeds of the Lake Powell region.

28. Chocolate Cliffs of Shinarump Conglomerate of the Chinle Formation were rivers deposits.

27. Grand Staircase, from Kaibab Plateau upwards, has resistant cliffs and erodible treads.

26. The Permian- Triassic disconformity was a time of abrupt global mass extinctions.

25. Aubrey Group records advance and retreat of a Permian seaway rimmed with coastal dunes.

24. Supai Group records erosion of the distant Appalachian and Ancestral Rocky Mountains.

23. Redwall Limestone records an extensive seaway; its caves now host groundwater flow.

22. A mid-Paleozoic disconformity records 100–160 million years of erosion.

21. Tapeats, Bright Angel, and Muav record rapid flooding of the continent by deepening oceans 510 to 500 million years ago.

20. Sixtymile Formation is now part of the Cambrian Tonto Group.

19. The Great Unconformity is where Tonto Group rests on older rocks with 0.2 to 1.3 billion years missing.

18. The Butte fault was active during Chuar Group time and created the basin it was deposited in.

17. The shale-rich Chuar Group records the first heterotrophic single-celled life.

16. The Unkar-Chuar Unconformity reflects tilting of Unkar Group and 300 million years of erosion.

15. Cardenas Basalt flows were fed by the diabase magmas in a dike and sill conduit system.

14. Diabase sills were intruded between Unkar Group layers as they were being tilted.

13. Dox Sandstone records red muds and sands deposited by far-traveled rivers.

12. Shinumo Sandstone represents sands deposited after erosion of underlying layers.

11. A 100-million-year disconformity within the Unkar Group records changes in plate convergence to the south.

10. Hakatai Formation is one of the most colorful layers (orange from iron oxide staining).

9. Bass Formation of Unkar Group has 1.25 Ga old stromatolites, the oldest fossils in the region.

8. The Great Nonconformity reflects erosion of the Vishnu Mountains from 1.66 to 1.25 Ga.

7. Cremation and other pegmatite swarms formed deep in the 1.70 billion-year-old Vishnu Mountains.

6. Zoroaster and other granodiorite plutons formed in 1.74-1.71 billion-year-old magmatic arc intrusions.

5. Vishnu Schist is 1.75 billion-year-old metasedimentary rocks that formed as submarine sandstones.

4. Brahma Schist is 1.75 billion-year-old mafic metavolcanic rocks that formed as submarine basalt flows.

3. Rama Schist is 1.75 billion-year-old felsic metavolcanic rocks that formed as rhyolite eruptions.

2. A 100-million-year unconformity reflects erosional unroofing of the Elves Chasm pluton.

1. The oldest rocks in the Grand Canyon region are part of the 1.84 billion-year-old Elves Chasm pluton.

More details on Grand Canyon's rock column. Work down from the top (#36) to the bottom (#1).

36. The mighty Colorado River has used its erosive tools (sand and gravel carried by energetic flow) to carve through solid rock. The river and its tributaries, plus gravity, provide the main erosive force that deepens and widens the canyon, and shapes Colorado Plateau landscapes. The supply of river water cannot meet the increasing societal and ecosystem needs for the entire western slope of the Rockies.

35. Groundwater that emerges as springs in many places within Grand Canyon and Grand Staircase originates as rain and snowmelt that falls on the surface and percolates downward along fractures and through porous/ permeable rock (aquifers) until encountering shale layers (aquicludes), then moves laterally toward canyon walls. Water pathways are complex but include cave systems in the Redwall- Muav aquifer, where some of the largest volume springs, like Roaring Springs, emanate.

34. Faults and fractures are abundant in all rock units of the Grand Canyon region. The one shown here is a schematic example of the faults that slipped during the Laramide orogeny about 70 million years ago. These faults lifted up one side relative to the other and caused monoclinal warps and folds that now define the edges of uplifts such as the Kaibab uplift. The arrows show that this fault has the opposite slip from the Butte fault that slipped in the Precambrian (#18).

33. Many water wells on the Navajo and Hopi lands draw water from the N-aquifer hosted in the porous Navajo Sandstone. Lake Powell waters recharge this aquifer.

32. Above the Dakota Sandstone is another 1000 m of strata not shown in this column, mainly Cretaceous shales and sandstones. The Pink Cliffs, not depicted here, are held up by sculpted pinkish rocks of the ~ 50 Ma (Eocene) Claron Formation seen in Bryce Canyon National Park.

31. The Grey Cliffs are formed by the Dakota Sandstone of the Mesa Verde Group. These were deposited on the beach of the Cretaceous inland seaway that extended from Mexico to the Arctic.

30. The White Cliffs are seen farther north and in Zion National Park where the upper Navajo Sandstone is whitish due to bleaching as fluids passed through it.

29. The Vermillion Cliffs are formed by reddish Moenave, Kayenta, and lower Navajo Sandstone that are well exposed near Lees Ferry and Lake Powell.

28. The Chocolate Cliffs are formed by the brownish Shinarump Conglomerate Member of the Chinle Formation seen at Lees Ferry.

27. The Grand Staircase is an iconic erosional style described by Dutton[14] as the series of steps formed by resistant cliffs, and treads formed in more erodable layers. The staircase climbs upwards from Grand Canyon's Kaibab Plateau, includes the Lees Ferry/ Lake Powell area, and extends to Zion and Bryce National Parks.

26. The Permian- Triassic boundary is an unconformity in the Grand Canyon region with ~ 30 million year gap (time not recorded) in the rock record. More complete sections elsewhere record one of the most catastrophic mass extinctions in Earth's history that occurred 251.9 Ma ago. In the Grand Canyon region, this P-T unconformity marks a change from marine deposition of Paleozoic limestones (below) to terrestrial deposition of Mesozoic redbeds.

25. The Permian Aubrey Group is made up of Coconino Sandstone, Toroweap Formation, and Kaibab Limestone that represent changing depositional environments (mudflats,

sand dunes, shallow seas). The Coconino Sandstone has giant crossbed sets that record the fronts of ancient sand dunes, now turned to rock. This unit is light colored and easily visible as a "bath-tub-ring" layer a bit below the rim of Grand Canyon. The erosion-resistant Kaibab Limestone forms the North and South Rims of Grand Canyon and holds up the corresponding Kaibab and Coconino Plateaus.

24. The Pennsylvanian Supai Group is a series of red sandstones, shales, and limestones that were deposited at a time when the Ancestral Rocky Mountains were being uplifted and eroded in the Colorado-New Mexico areas to the east. Some of its grains came in rivers that traversed the continent from the Appalachian Mountains that were also forming at this time as the Pangea supercontinent was being assembled.

23. The Mississippian Redwall Limestone forms one of the most impenetrable cliffs in Grand Canyon and many trails and routes take advantage of fracture zones to allow it to be traveled through. It appears red on the outside because of staining, but it is a gray fossiliferous limestone when broken open. Cracks and caves in it make it a karst aquifer that allows movement of groundwater.

22. The disconformity between the Cambrian Muav and Mississippian Redwall limestones represents up to 160 million years of missing rock record (time not recorded here). The Devonian Temple Butte Formation fills part of this time gap in some parts of the Grand Canyon.

21. The Tonto Group is made up of the Sixtymile Formation, Tapeats Sandstone, Bright Angel Shale, and Muav Limestone. These sediments were deposited as the Cambrian oceans advanced rapidly across North America between 510 and

Still more on Grand Canyon's rock column; oldest (#1) at bottom to youngest (#36) at top.

500 million years ago. The rapid flooding of the continent by ocean water is known as a marine transgression.

20. The Sixtymile Formation is preserved in eastern Grand Canyon. It was recently (in 2018) dated and shown to be 530-508 Ma old, rather than part of the Precambrian Grand Canyon Supergroup as previously thought.

19. The Great Unconformity between the Precambrian rocks and the overlying Tonto Group is recognized throughout Grand Canyon and the Southwest. There is a variable amount of time missing (lacuna) at this unconformity depending on the ages of underlying rocks. Where the ~500 Ma old Tapeats Sandstone or Bright Angel Shale rests atop the ~1,750 Ma old Vishnu basement rocks, this contact represents about 1,250 Ma (1.25 Ga) of missing rock record, or a maximum of 1.35 Ga where the Tapeats rests on the Elves Chasm gneiss. We know some of what went on during this time period from studying the Grand Canyon Supergroup and the intervening unconformities. See page 39 to test yourself on how four unconformities add up to make the Great Unconformity.

18. A major fault, the Butte fault, was active during the deposition of the Chuar Group in rift basins; it dropped down and preserved the Chuar Group in eastern Grand Canyon, the only place these rocks can be seen. It was later reactivated as an east-up fault in the Laramide orogeny (see page 36) and currently is one of many faults that are conduits for groundwater movement.

17. The 2-km-thick Chuar Group is divided into 3 formations (Nankoweap, Galeros, Kwagunt), and 8 members, that record deposition in the shallow Chuar seaway. These layers contain diverse single-celled microfossil assemblages that include vase-shaped microfossils that were the first heterotrophic organisms on Earth. They got their food from eating other organisms and each other, rather than photosynthesis. Evidence for these mini-vampires is shown on page 77.

16. The unconformity between the 1.25-1.10 Ga Unkar Group (also about 2 km thick) the 0.78- 0.73 Ma Chuar Group is an angular unconformity that represents about 300 million years of missing rock record (time not recorded here).

15. Cardenas Basalt is made up of many basalt flows that flowed into a fault-bounded basin when North America was being squeezed from the south due to plate collisions. This caused NE-SW extension (insipient rifting). A series of Unkar-age faults trend NW and were important for influencing Tonto Group deposition, as well as modern groundwater flow

14. Intrusions of basaltic melt called diabase (black, basaltic composition) squeezed between layers of the Unkar Group in intrusions called sills and also conveyed magma upwards in dikes. These intrusions occurred 1.1 Ga ago and fed overlying basalt flows of the Cardenas Basalts.

13. Dox Formation forms very thick (more than 1000 m) upper sections of the Unkar Group and can be seen from the East Rim Drive viewpoints such as Lipan Point (see page 41).

12. Shinumo Sandstone forms white sandstone resistent cliffs that were cemented by silica soon after deposition and later formed islands in Cambrian time.

11. A 90 Ma time break occurs between the 1.23 Ga Hakatai Shale and the 1.14 Ga Shinumo Sandstone.

10. The Hakatai Formation of the lower part of the Unkar Group has bright orange colors that can be seen from Yavapai Geology Museum.

9. The Bass Formation was deposited 1.25 billion years ago. It contains fossil forms called stromatolites that record single-celled algae that built algal colonies on mounds in a shallow sea. Examples can be seen on the Trail of Time at the 1,190 Ma marker and at the 1,160 wayside.

8. The Great Nonconformity at the top of the basement represents a period of erosion from 1.66 to 1.25 billion years ago during which the Vishnu Mountains were worn down such that rocks that were once 20 km deep were brought to the Earth's surface. This unconformity reflects about 500 million years of missing rock record (time not recorded here). A nonconformity is where sedimentary rocks overly igneous and metamorphic rocks. This contact represents the largest amount of eroded material and the longest time gap of all Grand Canyon unconformities.

7. The Cremation pegmatite swarm is a series of granite dikes and sills that record the upward rise of magmas derived from melting of the lower crust during NW-SE compression as plates collided about 1.7–1.66 billion years ago during formation of the continental crust in the southwestern U.S. The subvertical layering in the Vishnu basement rocks, called foliation or schistosity, formed by intense folding of original bedding due to plate collisions. Basement rocks were very hot and at depths of 20 km below the peaks of the now-eroded Vishnu Mountains that formed during this Yavapai orogeny.

6. A series of granodiorite plutons intruded the schists from 1.74 to 1.71 billion years ago. The Zoroaster granite is a large granite body one can see from Yavapai Geology Museum. Other examples of these rocks can be seen on the Trail of Time between markers 1,740 and 1,710.

5. Vishnu Schist formed in a sedimentary basin about 1.75 billion years ago. It contains detrital zircon sand grains of 1.85 and 2.5 Ga, and occasional zircon sand grains as old as 3.2 Ga that were washed into the basin from adjacent highlands that contained rocks similar to those now found in South Australia.

3, 4. The Rama and Brahma schists were volcanic rocks (rhyolite and basalt respectively) that formed in an oceanic island arc about 1.75 billion years ago. They were metamorphosed to metarhyolite and metabasalt (amphibolite) during the Yavapai orogeny.

2. The folded unconformity between the Elves Chasm gneiss and the overlying Granite Gorge Metamorphic Suite represents about 100 million years ago of missing rock record (time not recorded here).

1. Elves Chasm gneiss of Grand Canyon is 1,840 million years old, the oldest rock yet discovered in the southwestern U.S. It is a metamorphosed granodiorite plutonic rock that is a fragment of an oceanic island arc of this age. We are searching for the still-older rocks it must have intruded into.

Grand Canyon Rock Names and Ages

Eon	Era	Period	Epoch	Age Missing Time (millions of years)		Grand Canyon Rock Names and Ages			
Phanerozoic	Cenozoic	Quaternary	Holocene	0.012	Cenozoic deposits	Travertines form over the past 1 Ma			
			Pleistocene	2.58		Basalts flow into western G.C. 815,000 to 100,000 years ago			
		Tertiary — Neogene	Pliocene	5.33		4.4 Ma basalt overlies earliest Colorado River gravel			
			Miocene	23		Volcanic eruptions signal Basin & Range collapse			
		Tertiary — Paleogene	Oligocene	34		23 Ma gravels on Hualapai Plateau			
			Eocene	56		50 Ma lake beds near Bryce Canyon N.P.			
			Paleocene	66		65 Ma N-flowing paleoriver deposits on Hualapai Plateau			
	Mesozoic	Cretaceous	2 epochs	145	eroded strata	70 - 100 Ma inland sea deposits of Colorado Plateau			
		Jurassic	3 epochs	201		Desert sandstones of Zion N.P. and Lake Powell			
		Triassic	3 epochs	252 ~ 30		Moenkopi and Chinle formations form Cedar Mtn. & Red Butte			

					Aubrey Gp.		Age (Ma)	Duration	Member
	Paleozoic	Permian	Lopingian	259					Harrisburg
			Guadalupian	273		Kaibab Formation	270	269-273	Fossil Mountain
			Cisuralian	~ 5		Toroweap Formation	275	273-278	Wood Ranch
						Coconino Sandstone	280	278-282	Brady Canyon
						Hermit Formation	285	284-290	Seligman
				299	Supai Gp.	Esplanade Sandstone	290	290-294	
		Carboniferous	Pennsylvanian	~ 10		Wescogame Formation	300	299-303	Horseshoe Mesa
				323 ~ 5		Manakacha Formation	315	314-317	Mooney Falls
						Watahomigi Formation	320	318-323	ThunderSprings / Whitemore Wash
			Mississippian	~ 10		Surprise Canyon Fm.	325	324-326	Havasu
				359 ~ 25		Redwall Limestone	340	335-348	Kanab Canyon
		Devonian	3 epochs	419 ~ 150		Temple Butte Formation	385	375-385	Peach Springs
		Silurian	4 epochs	444					Spencer Canyon
		Ordovician	3 epochs	485		global extinctions and glaciation			Sanup Plateau / Rampart Cave
		Cambrian	Furongian	497	Tonto Gp.				Flour Sack
				not recorded at Grand Canyon		Frenchman Mtn. Dolo.	500	497-503	Meriwitica
			Miaolingian			Muav Limestone	504	503-505	Tincanebits
						Bright Angel Shale	506	505-507	Red Brown Ss.
				509		Tapeats Sandstone	508	507-509	Transition
			Series 2	521		Sixtymile Formation	510	509-530	Lower, Middle, Upper
			Terreneuvian	541					

Grand Canyon Rock Names and Ages

Eon	Era	Period	Epoch	Age Missing Time (millions of years)		Grand Canyon Rock Names and Ages		
Proterozoic	Neoproterozoic		Ediacaran	541		First animal life evolves on Earth		
				635				
			Cryogenian	720		Snowball Earth - Time of global glaciations		
			Tonian	~200	G.C. Supergroup — Chuar Gp.		Age (Ma)	Member
								Walcott
						Kwagunt Formation	729-753	Awatubi
						Galeros Formation	753-770	Carbon Butte
						Nankoweap Formation	770-775	Duppa
				1,000 ~200	G.C. Supergroup — Unkar Group	Cardenas Basalt	1,104	Carbon Canyon
	Mesoproterozoic		Stenian			diabase intrusions	~1,100	Jupiter
						Dox Formation	1,120	Tanner
						Shinumo Sandstone	1,130	Ochoa Point
				1,200 ~90		Hakatai Shale	1,230	Commanche Pt.
			Ectasian			Bass Formation	1,255	Soloman Temple
				1,400 ~400				Escalante Ck.
			Calymmian	1,600	Basement rocks — Plutons	Quartermaster Granite	1,375 ± 2	Hotauta granites
						Phantom Pluton	1,662 ± 1	
						Cremation Pegmatites	1,698 ± 1	
						Horn Pluton	1,713 ± 2	
						Ruby Pluton	1,716 ± 0.5	granodiorite
	Paleoproterozoic		Statherian			Trinity Pluton	1,730 ± 93	intrusions
						Diamond Creek Pluton	1,736 ± 1	
						Zoroaster Pluton	1,740 ± 2	
					Basement rocks — GGMS	Vishnu Schist	1,750 ± 2	GGMS= Granite Gorge
						Brahma Schist	1,750 ± 2	Metamorphic Suite
						Rama Schist	1,751-1,741	
			Ososirian	1,800 ~85		Elves Chasm Gneiss	1,840 ± 1	
				2050		Wyoming rift margin & glaciations		
			Rhyacian	2,300		First great oxygenation of Earth's atmosphere		
			Siderian	2,500		Many Vishnu Schist detrital zircon grains are ~2.5 Ga		
Archaen	Neoarchean			2,800				
	Mesoarchean			3,200				
	Paleoarchean			3,600	□ = not recorded at Grand Canyon	Oldest detrital grains in Vishnu Schist are ~3.3 Ga		
	Eoarchean			4,000		Life exists on Earth ~3.8 Ga		
Hadean				4,567		Earth is bombarded by meteorites 4.6 to 4.0 Ga		

References

These references cite the foundational literature plus the most recent peer-reviewed papers. Most can be found on the internet. The references within them can be used to take you back through the more complete history of research on a given topic.

The Million Year Trail

1. Powell, J.W., 1875, Exploration of the Colorado River of the West and its tributaries: Washington D.C., U.S. Government Printing Office, 291 p.

2. Karlstrom, K.E., Coblentz, D., Dueker, K., Ouimet, W., Kirby, E., Van Wijk, J., Schmandt, B., Kelley, S., Lazear, G., Crossey, L.J., Crow, R., Aslan, A, Darling, A., Aster, R., MacCarthy, J., Hansen, S.M., Stachnik, J., Stockli, D.F., Hoffman M., McKeon, R., Feldman, J. Heizler, M., Donahue, M.S., and the CREST working group, 2012, Surface response to mantle convection beneath the Colorado Rocky Mountains and Colorado Plateau: Lithosphere, v. 4 p. 3-22.

3. Crossey, L.J., Fischer, T.P., Patchett, P.J., Karlstrom, K.E., Hilton, D.R., Newell, D.L., Huntoon, P., Reynolds, A.C., and de Leeuw, G.A.M., 2006, Dissected hydrologic system at the Grand Canyon: interaction between deeply derived fluids and plateau aquifer waters in modern springs and travertine: Geology, v. 34, p. 25-28.

4. Crossey, L.J., Karlstrom, K.E., Springer, A., Newell, D., Hilton, D., and Fischer, T., 2009, Degassing of mantle-derived CO_2 and ^3He from springs in the southern Colorado Plateau region — flux rates, neotectonics connections, and implications for understanding the groundwater system: Geological Society of America Bulletin, v. 121; no. 7/8; p. 1034–1053.

5. J.W. Powell, 1875, The Canyons of the Colorado, third paper, Scribners Monthly, p. 523-537; also reprinted as Dover Publications Inc., 1895, Canyons of the Colorado, and in 1961 as: The Exploration of the Colorado River and its canyons.

6. J.W. Powell and G.W. Ingalls, 1874, Report of Special Commissioners on the condition of Ute Indians of Utah; Paiutes of Utah, northern Arizona, southern Nevada, and southeastern California; the Go-si-utes of Utah and Nevada; the northwestern Shoshones of Idaho and Utah; and the western Shoshones of Nevada; and report concerning claims of settlers in the Mo-a-pa Valley, southeastern Nevada: Washington D.C.

7. Painting of Tusayan Ruin by Roy Anderson, used with NPS permission.

8. Courtesy of Scripps CO_2 program: Antarctic ice core record from Law Dome before 1958 (Macfarling Meure, C. et al., 2006: Law Dome CO_2, CH_4 and N_2O

ice core records extended to 2000 years BP. Geophysical Research Letters, 33.) http://scrippsco2.ucsd.edu/graphics_gallery/mauna_loa_and_south_pole/merged_ice_core_record

9. Sir Archibald Geike: Lecture at the Evening Meeting, Royal Geographical Society (24 Mar 1879), 'Discussion on Geographical Evolution', in Proceedings of the Royal Geographical Society and Monthly Record (1879).

10. Karlstrom, K.E., Crow, R., McIntosh, W., Peters, L., Pederson, J., Raucci, J., Crossey, L.J., Umhoefer, P., Dunbar, N., 2007, $^{40}Ar/^{39}Ar$ and field studies of Quaternary basalts in Grand Canyon and model for carving Grand Canyon: quantifying the interaction of river incision and normal faulting across the western edge of the Colorado Plateau: Geological Society of America Bulletin, v. 119, p. 1283-1312.

11. Crow, R.S., Karlstrom, K.E., McIntosh, W., Peters, L., Dunbar, N., 2008, History of Quaternary volcanism and lava dams in western Grand Canyon based on LIDAR analysis, $^{40}Ar/^{39}Ar$ dating, and field studies: Implications for flow stratigraphy, timing of volcanic events, and lava dams: Geosphere, v. 4, p. 183–206.

12. Crow, R.S., Karlstrom, K.E., McIntosh, W., Peters, L., Heizler, M., Young, R., Crossey, L.C., and Dunbar, N., 2015, Quaternary lava dams of Grand Canyon: insights into their extent, structure, timing, and failure mechanisms: Geosphere, v. 11, p. 1–38.

13. Brumbaugh, D.S., 2005, Short Notes; Active Faulting and Seismicity in a Prefractured Terrane: Grand Canyon, Arizona Bulletin of the Seismological Society of America, v. 95, p. 1561–1566.

14. Dutton, C.E., 1882, Tertiary history of the Grand Canon district: U.S. Geological Survey Monograph 2, 264 p. and Atlas.

The Main Trail of Time

15. Beus, S. S., and Morales, M., 2003, Grand Canyon Geology, second edition: Oxford University Press, 432 p.

16. Timmons, J.M., Karlstrom, K.E., Heizler, M., Bowring, S.A., and Crossey,

References, cont.

L.C., 2005, Tectonic inferences from the 1254- ~1100 Ma Unkar Group and Nankoweap Formation, Grand Canyon: Intracratonic deformation and basin formation during protracted Grenville orogenesis: Geological Society of America Bulletin v. 117, p. 1573-1595.

17. Dehler, C., Gehrels, G., Porterm S., Heizler, M., Karl strom, K., Cox, G., Crossey, L., and Timmons, M., 2017, Synthesis of the 780–740 Ma Chuar, Uinta Mountain, and Pahrump (ChUMP) groups, western USA: Implications for Laurentia-wide cratonic marine basins: Geological Society of America Bulletin, v. 129, p. 607-624.

18. Karlstrom, K.E., Ilg, B.R., Williams, M.L., Hawkins, D.P., Bowring, S.A., and Seaman, S.J., 2003, Paleoproterozoic rocks of the Granite Gorges, in Beus, S.S. and Morales, M., eds., Grand Canyon Geology: Oxford University Press, second edition, p. 9-38.

19. Crossey, L.C., Karlstrom, K.E., Dorsey, R., Pearce, J., Wan, E., Beard, L.S., Asmerom, Y., Polyak, V., Crow, R.S, Cohen, A., Bright, J., Huth, 2015, The importance of groundwater in propagating downward integration of the 6-5 Ma Colorado River System: Geochemistry of springs, travertines and lacustrine carbonates of the Grand Canyon region over the past 12 million years: Geosphere, v. 11, p. 660–682.

20. Lucchitta, I., 1972, Early history of the Colorado River in the Basin and Range Province: Geological Society of America Bulletin, v. 83, p. 1933–1948.

21. Dickinson, W.R., Karlstrom, K.E., Hanson, A.D., Gehrels, G.E., Pecha, M., Cather, S.M., and Kimbrough, D.L., 2014, Detrital-zircon U-Pb evidence precludes paleo–Colorado River sediment in the exposed Muddy Creek Formation of the Virgin River depression: Geosphere, v. 10, p. 1123-1138.

22. Lucchitta, I., 1989, History of the Grand Canyon and of the Colorado River in Arizona, in Bues, S.S., and Morales, M., eds., Grand Canyon Geology: New York, Oxford University Press, p. 311–332.

23. Crow, R., Karlstrom, K.E., Darling, A., Crossey, L.J., Polyak, V., Granger, D., Asmerom, Y., and Schmandt, B., 2014, Steady incision of Grand Canyon at the million year timeframe: a case for mantle-driven differential uplift: Earth and Planetary Science Letters, v. 397, p. 159–173.

24. Young, R.A., and Crow, R.S., 2014. Paleogene Grand Canyon incompatible with Tertiary paleogeography and stratigraphy: Geosphere, v. 10, p. 664–679.

25. Karlstrom, K.E., Crossey, L.J., Embid, E., Crow, R., Heizler, M., Hereford, R., Beard, L.S., Ricketts, J.W., Cather, S., Kelley, S., 2016, Cenozoic incision history of the Little Colorado River: its role in carving Grand Canyon and onset of rapid incision in the past ~2 Ma in the Colorado River System: Geosphere CRevolution volume, v. 12, no. 6, p. 49–81.

26. Winn, C., Karlstrom, K.E., Shuster, D.L., Kelley, S., Fox, M., 2014, 6 Ma age of carving Westernmost Grand Canyon: Reconciling geologic data with combined AFT, (U–Th)/He, and ^{4}He/^{3}He thermochronologic data: Earth and Planetary Science Letters, v. 474, p. 257–271.

27. Karlstrom, K.E., Lee, J., Kelley, S., Crow, R., Crossey, L.J., Young, R., Lazear, G., Beard, L.S., and Ricketts, J., Fox, M., Shuster D., 2014, Formation of the Grand Canyon 5 to 6 million years ago through integration of older palaeocanyons: Nature Geoscience, v. 7, p. 239- 244, with Supplementary materials.

28. Karlstrom, K.E., Crow, R, Crossey, L.J., Coblentz, D., and van Wijk, J., 2008, Model for tectonically driven incision of the less than 6 Ma Grand Canyon: Geology, v. 36, no. 11, p. 835-838.

29. Flowers, R.M., Wernicke, B.P., and Farley, K.A., 2008, Unroofing, incision, and uplift history of the southwestern Colorado Plateau from apatite (U-Th)/He thermochronometry: Geological Society of America Bulletin, v. 120, p. 571–587.

30. Karlstrom, K.E., Hagadorn, J., Gehrels, G.G., Mathews, W., Schmitz, M., Madronich, L., Mulder, J., Pecha,M., Geisler, D., and Crossey, L.J., 2018, Cambrian Sauk transgression in the Grand Canyon region redefined by detrital zircons: Nature Geoscience, v. 11, p. 438-443.

31. Karlstrom, K.E., and Timmons, J.M., 2013, Many unconformities make one "Great Unconformity", in Timmons, J.M., and Karlstrom, K.E., eds., Grand Canyon Geology: 2 Billion Years of Earth History: Geological Society of America Special Paper 489, p. 73-80.

32. Karlstrom, K.E., Ilg, B.R., Hawkins, D., Williams, M.L., Dumond, G., Mahan, K., and Bowring, S.A., 2013, Vishnu basement rocks of the upper Granite Gorge: continent formation 1.84 to 1.66 billion years ago, in Timmons, J.M., and Karlstrom, K.E., eds., Grand Canyon Geology: 2 Billion Years of Earth History: Geological Society of America Special Paper 489, p. 7-24.

References, cont.

Stories from Grand Canyon's Rocks (told by the rocks themselves).

33. Granger, B.H., 1983, Arizona Names (X Marks the Place): Tucson, AZ, The Falconer Publishing Company, 824 p.

34. International Stratigraphic Commission on Stratigraphy: http://www.stratigraphy.org/index.php/ics-chart-timescale

35. Crossey, L.J., and Karlstrom, K.E., 2013, Travertines and travertine springs in eastern Grand Canyon: What they tell us about groundwater, paleoclimate, and incision of Grand Canyon, in Timmons, J.M., and Karlstrom, K.E., eds., Grand Canyon Geology: 2 Billion Years of Earth History: Geological Society of America Special Paper 489, p. 131-144.

36. J.W. Powell, The Exploration of the Colorado River and its Canyons, ©1961, Dover Publications, Inc.); from: Exploration of the Colorado River of the West and its Tributaries, explored in 1869, 1870, 1871, and 1372, under the Direction of the Secretary of the Smithsonian Institution. Washington, 1875.

37. Crow, R., Karlstrom, K., Asmerom, Y., Schamndt, B., Polyak, V., and Du-Frane, S.A., 2011, Shrinking of the Colorado Plateau via lithospheric mantle erosion: Evidence from Nd and Sr isotopes and geochronology of Neogene basalts, Geology, v. 39, p. 27–30.

38. Paleogeographic Basemaps by Ron Blakey © 2016 Colorado Plateau Geosystems

39. Hopkins, R.L. and Thompson, K.L., 2003, Kaibab Formation, in Beus, S.S. and Morales, M., eds. Grand Canyon Geology: Oxford University Press, p. 196-211.

40. Turner, C.E., 2003, Torweap Formation, in Beus, S.S. and Morales, M., eds. Grand Canyon Geology: Oxford University Press, p. 180-195.

41. Middleton, L.T., Elliott, D.K., and Morales, M., 2003, Coconino Sandstone, in Beus, S.S. and Morales, M., eds. Grand Canyon Geology: Oxford University Press, p. 163-179.

42. Blakey, R.C., 2003, Supai Group and Hermit Formation, in Beus, S.S. and Morales, M., eds. Grand Canyon Geology: Oxford University Press, p. 136-162.

43. Beus, S.S., 2003, Redwall Limestone and Surprise Valley Formation, in Beus, S.S. and Morales, M., eds. Grand Canyon Geology: Oxford University Press, p. 115-135.

44. Beus, S.S., 2003, Temple Butte Formation, in Beus, S.S. and Morales, M., eds. Grand Canyon Geology: Oxford University Press, p. 107-114.

45. Gehrels, G.E., Blakey, R., Karlstrom, K.E. Timmons, J.M., Kelley, S., Dickinson, B., and Pecha, M., 2011, Detrital zircon U-Pb geochronology of Paleozoic strata in the Grand Canyon, Arizona: Lithosphere, v. 3, p. 183-200.

46. Porter, S., 2016, Tiny vampires in ancient seas: Evidence for predation via perforation in fossils from the 780–740 million-year-old Chuar Group, Grand Canyon, USA: Proceedings of the Royal Society, ser. B, Biological Sciences, v. 283, v. 283, 20160221.

47. Rooney, A.D., Austermann, J., Smith, E.F., Yang, L., Selby, D., Dehler, C.M., Schmitz, M.D., Karlstrom, K.E., and Macdonald, F.A., 2017, Coupled Re-Os and U-Pb geochronology of the Tonian Chuar Group, Grand Canyon: Geological Society of America Bulletin, v. 129, p. 1085-1098.

48. Timmons, M.J., Karlstrom, K.E., Dehler, C.M., Geissman, J.W., and Heizler, M.T., 2001, Proterozoic multistage (~1.1 and ~0.8 Ga) extension in the Grand Canyon Supergroup and establishment of northwest and north-south tectonic grains in the southwestern United States: Geological Society of America Bulletin, v. 113, no. 2, p 163-180.

49. Mulder, J. A., Karlstrom, K. E., Fletcher, K., Heizler, M. T., Timmons, J. M., Crossey, L. J., Gehrels, G. E., and Pecha, M., 2017, The syn-orogenic sedimentary record of the Grenville Orogeny in southwest Laurentia: Precambrian Research, v. 294, p. 33–52.

50. Dumond, G., Mahan, K., Williams, M.W., and Karlstrom, K.E., 2007, Metamorphism in middle continental crust, Upper Granite Gorge, Grand Canyon, Arizona: implications for segmented crustal architecture, processes at 25-km-deep levels, and unroofing of orogens: Geological Society of America Bulletin, v. 119, p. 202–222.

51. Karlstrom, K.E., and Bowring, S.A., 1993, Proterozoic orogenic history in Arizona, in Van Schmus, W.R. et al., Transcontinental Proterozoic provinces: Boulder, Colorado, Geological Society of America, The Geology of North America, v. C-2.

References, cont.

52. Nyman, M.W., and Karlstrom, K.E., 1997, Pluton emplacement processes and tectonic setting of the 1.42 Ga Signal batholith, SW USA: important role of crustal anistropy during regional shortening: Precambrian Research, v. 82, p. 237-263.

53. Hawkins, D.P., Bowring, S.A., Ilg, B.R., Karlstrom, K.E., and Williams, M.L., 1996, U-Pb geochronologic constraints on Proterozoic crustal evolution: Geological Society of America Bulletin, v. 108, p. 1167-1181.

54. Ilg, Brad, Karlstrom, K.E., Hawkins, D., and Williams, M.L. 1996, Tectonic evolution of Paleoproterozoic rocks in Grand Canyon; Insights into middle crustal processes: Geological Society of America Bulletin, v. 108, p. 1149-1166.

55. Holland, M.E., Karlstrom, K.E., Doe, M., Gehrels, G., Pecha, M., Shufeldt, O., Begg, G., and Griffin, W.L., and Belousova, E., 2015, An imbricate midcrustal suture zone: The Mojave-Yavapai Province boundary in Grand Canyon, Arizona: Geological Society of America Bulletin, v. 127, p. 1391–1410.

56. Shufeldt, O.P., Karlstrom, K.E., Gehrels, G.E., and Howard, K., 2010, Archean detrital zircons in the Proterozoic Vishnu Schist of the Grand Canyon, Arizona: Implications for crustal architecture and Nuna reconstructions: Geology, v. 38. p. 1099 - 1102.

The Making of the Trail of Time Geoscience Exhibition (1995-2010)

57. Karlstrom, K., Semken, S., Crossey, L., Perry, D., Gyllenhaal, E. D., Dodick, J., Williams, M., Hellmich-Bryan, J., Crow, R., Bueno Watts, N., & Ault, C., 2008, Informal geoscience education on a grand scale: The Trail of Time exhibition at Grand Canyon: Journal of Geoscience Education, v. 56, no. 4, p. 354-361.

58. Crow, R., Karlstrom, K.E., Crossey, L.J., Semken, S., Perry, D., Williams, M., and Bryan, J., 2011, It's about time: Innovations in geoscience education at Grand Canyon: Legacy, v. 22, p. 26-27.

59. Perry, D. L. (2012). What makes learning fun? Principles for the design of intrinsically motivating museum exhibits. Lanham, MD: AltaMira Press.

60. Selinda Research Associates Evaluation Briefs - http://tot.unm.edu/eval_docs.html

61. Semken S., Ward, E. G., Moosavi, S., & Chinn, P. W. U., 2017, Place-based education in geoscience: Theory, research, practice, and assessment. Journal of Geoscience Education, v. 65, p. 542 -562.

62. Semken, S., Dodick, J., Ben David, O., Pineda, M., Bueno Watts, N., & Karlstrom, K., 2009, Timeline and time scale cognition experiments for a geological interpretative exhibit at Grand Canyon: Proceedings of the National Association for Research in Science Teaching, Garden Grove, California.

Looking Deeper into Geology.

63. Lee, J.P., Stockli, D.F., Kelley, S.A., Pederson, J.L., Karlstrom, K.E., Ehlers, T.A., 2013, New Thermochronometric Constraints on the Tertiary Landscape Evolution of Central and Eastern Grand Canyon, Arizona: Geosphere, v. 9, p. 216-268.

64. Benton, M.J., and Twitchett, R.J., 2003, How to kill (almost) all life: the end-Permian extinction event: Trends in Ecology and Evolution, v. 18, no. 7, p. 358-365

65. These fossil pages constructed by Camille Dwyer, UNM. with input from Barry Kues and Spencer Lucas.

66. Trans-Canyon Water Pipeline, Grand Canyon National Park: Historic American Engineering Record, Intermountain Regional Office, National Park Service: HAER AZ-95, 34 p.

67. https://az.water.usgs.gov/projects/Uranium/

68. Finch, W.I., Sutphin, H.B., Pierson, C.T., McCammon, R.B., and Wenrich, K.J., 1990, The 1987 estimate of undiscovered uranium endowment in solution-collapse breccia pipes in the Grand Canyon region of northern Arizona and adjacent Utah: U.S. Geological Survey Circular, 1051, 19 p.

69. Sir Archibald Geike, Outlines of Field Geology, 1879, p. 216

Acknowledgements

The authors acknowledge the rest of the Trail of Time team: Steve Semken, Ryan Crow, Michael Williams, Deborah Perry and Judy Hellmich-Bryan, and many others We acknowledge the National Science Foundation, partnered with the National Park Service, for the funding. We enjoyed the synergies that developed over the decades it took (since 1995) to develop this exhibition. We thank all the participating scientists, students, evaluators, interpreters, designers, fabricators, and Park rangers who made this possible. The collective spirit of this group involved constant refinement to achieve better content, evaluation, design, and effective interpretation for multiple learning levels. We hope this spirit will continue into the future of the Trail of Time Exhibition and similar geoscience interpretation efforts at Grand Canyon and other parks.

Park Contributors: Superintendents: Joe Alston (initial agreement), Steve Martin (2010 opening), and David Uberagua and Christine Lehnertz (continued improvements).

Park Interpretation Chiefs: Richard Ellis (conception), Jim Gale (momentum), Judy Hellmich-Bryant (design, evaluation, and installation).

Park Rangers: Carl Bowman (geology), Ellen Seeley (exhibits), Allyson Mathis (geology), Jim Heywood (geology), Johanna Lombarde (Creative Media), Emma Benenati, and Rhonda Newton (collecting permits).

Trail Crew: Bill Allen, Chris Brothers, Shane Rasmussen.

Photography: Michael Quinn provided many of the photographs for the nomination and for this guide.

Evaluation: Deborah Perry, Eric Gyllenhaal, and Dianne White of Selinda Research Associates, Marcella Wells, and Trail of Time team.

Cognition Research: Steve Semken, Rebecca Frus, Jeff Dodick, Kevin Dunbar.

Design: Jim Sell (Jim Sell Designs), Sue Sell (graphic design), Mickey Schilling (artwork), Brian Williamson and Matt Blakely (design and prototypes), Andrew Merriell and Ramona Sakiestewa of Andrew Merriell and Associates (early design ideas), Mark Talbot (early graphic design).

Graphic Design: Ryan Crow drafted many of the figures for the ToT; Jordan Anderson drafted many of the figures for this guide.

Acknowledgements, cont.

Exhibit Fabrication and Installation: Dean MacLennan and Scott Davis of Rock & Company.

Marker Fabrication: Oregon Bronze (Main trail markers), John Sweeney of Umass (Million Year and Early Earth Trail markers); we also thank Park visitors for the inspiration and free installation of pennies in the ones-markers– we always wanted copper in the exhibit since Arizona is the Copper state.

National Science Foundation: Leonard Johnson, Mike Mayhew, Russ Kelz.

Project Management: Marcella Wells of Wells Resources Inc.

2002 Advisory Board: Charles Ault, L. Sue Beard, Andrew Becenti, Rolf Beier, Geoge Billingsley, Ron Blakey, John Bloch, Carl Bowman, Brad Dimock, Paul Dusenbery, David Elliott, Judy Hellmich, Jim Heywood, Susan Jagoda, Gary Ladd, Bob Lillie, Allyson Mathis, Mike Mayhew, Cheri Morrow, Ellen Seeley, Deborah Tuck, Stacey Wagner, Michelle Hall-Wallace, Arthur Wolf.

Students: We thank all the University of New Mexico graduate students, upper division undergraduates, and Freshman Learning Community students who helped evaluate, refine, and install the Trail of Time; and thanks to the Department of Earth and Planetary Sciences, and all UNM offices that facilitated the project.

Park visitors: We also thank the hundreds of Park visitors who interrupted their visits and gave so willingly and generously of their time by participating in the many phases of evaluation, research, and design of the Trail of Time exhibit.

Reviewers: All aspects of this book greatly befitted from critical reviews of its prototype by: Carl Bowman, Ryan Crow, Spencer Lucas, Deborah Perry, and Steven Semken. Barry Kues also helped with fossil identification.

We thank Betty Upchurch for writing the nomination, and the National Association for Interpretation for awarding the Trail of Time the 2011 First Place award for outdoor exhibits.

"Geology sets before us problems of the highest interest regarding the history of the ground beneath our feet, and thus gives a new charm to scenery which may be already replete with attractions."
Sir Archibald Geikie (1879)[69]

A view from the center window at Yavapai Geology Museum. Look within the layers and see if you can see the ancient island (a monadnock) of Grand Canyon Supergroup rocks that was fringed by 505-million-year-old beach sands of the Tapeats Sandstone and eventually got covered by muds of the Bright Angel Shale as the Tonto Group strata accumulated.